$$\frac{\text{number of waves}}{\text{frequency} \mid \text{Time}} = \boxed{\frac{n}{f \mid T}}$$

$$\frac{\text{length of all waves}}{\text{Single wave} \mid \text{number of}} = \boxed{\frac{d}{\lambda \mid n}}$$
length   waves

$$\frac{\text{wave speed}}{\text{wave} \mid \text{frequency}} = \boxed{\frac{v}{\lambda \mid f}}$$
length

$$\frac{\text{distance}}{\text{wavespeed} \mid \text{Time}} = \boxed{\frac{d}{v \mid T}}$$

both wave speed

$Q = IT$

BrightRED Study Guide

Curriculum for Excellence

N5

PHYSICS

Paul Van der Boon

First published in 2013 by:
Bright Red Publishing Ltd
1 Torphichen Street
Edinburgh
EH3 8HX

Reprinted with corrections 2014 and 2015.

A CIP record for this book is available from the British Library
ISBN 978-1-906736-44-6

With thanks to:
Ken Vail Graphic Design (layout and artwork) and Dr Anna Clark (copy-edit)
Cover design and series book design by Caleb Rutherford – eidetic

Acknowledgements
Permission has been sought from all relevant copyright holders and Bright Red Publishing
are grateful for the use of the following:

Alexander Sakhatovsky/Shutterstock.com (p 7); Teeraphat/Shutterstock.com (p 7);
RichVintage/istockphoto (p 8); zig4photo/istockphoto (p 10); Tusumaru/Shutterstock.
com (p 18); Shur23/istockphoto (p 19); Stu49/Shutterstock.com (p 20); Shutterstock.com
(p 20); Carlo Toffolo/Shutterstock.com (p 21); Virunja/Shutterstock.com (p 21); GVictoria/
Shutterstock.com (p 22); Lisa S./Shutterstock.com (p 23); Ingimage (p 23); Ttatty/
Shutterstock.com; MattiaATH/Shutterstock.com (p 26); somnuk jansinka/Shutterstock.
com (p 27); Blaz Kure/Shutterstock.com (p 30); photogl/Shutterstock.com (p 30);
SasinT/Shutterstock.com (p 31); akud/Shutterstock.com (p 32); Konjushenko Vladimir/
Shutterstock.com (p 32); Four Oaks/Shutterstock.com (p 38); Smileus/Shutterstock.com
(p 39); R. Gino Santa Maria/Shutterstock.com (p 40); Ilya Rabkin/Shutterstock.com (p
44); Poznyakov/Shutterstock.com (p 44); Vibrant Image Studio/Shutterstock.com (p 44);
Polryaz/Shutterstock.com (p 44); Artur Synenko/Shutterstock.com (p 45); PunyaFamily/
Shutterstock.com (p 45); Christian Delbert/Shutterstock.com (p 45); leonello/Shutterstock.
com (p 46); pzAxe/Shutterstock.com (p 51); Denise Lett/Shutterstock.com (p 52);
Andrey_Kuzmin/Shutterstock.com (p 58); Garsya/Shutterstock.com (p 58); Dudaeva/
Shutterstock.com (p 58); graja/Shutterstock.com (p 58); ssguy/Shutterstock.com (p 58);
Olena Mykhaylova/Shutterstock.com (p 58); ktsdesign/Shutterstock.com (p 58); ID1974/
Shutterstock.com (p 61); mihalec/Shutterstock.com (p 61); turtix/Shutterstock.com (p 61);
Maksim Toome/Shutterstock.com (p 66); James Steidl/Shutterstock.com (p 66); ollyy/
Shutterstock.com (p 66); Paul Drabot/Shutterstock.com (p 66); anekoho/Shutterstock.
com (p 72); kuppa/Shutterstock.com (p 72); Piotr Marcinski/Shutterstock.com (p 72);
NASA (pp 73, 78, 79); NASA/JPL-Caltech-ESA/Hubble and Digitized Sky Survey 2 (p 79);
isskh/Shutterstock.com (p 80); Galushko Sergey/Shutterstock.com (p 80); Lucky Business/
Shutterstock.com (p 80); Serg64/Shutterstock.com (p 80); nikkytok/Shutterstock.com
(p 80); Levent Konuk/Shutterstock.com (p 80); NASA (p 81); JHUAPL/SwRI (p 81); NASA
(three images on p 82); NASA (p 83); NASA/Sandra Joseph and Kevin O'Connell (p 83);
Igor Kovalchuk/Shutterstock.com (p 84); Giovanni Benintende/Shutterstock.com (p 84);
Igor Zh./Shutterstock.com (p 84); NASA (p 85); NASA/WMAP Science Team (p 85); NASA
(p 85); Neo Edmund/Shutterstock.com (p 85); lightpoet/Shutterstock.com (p 91).

Printed and bound in the UK by Charlesworth.

CONTENTS

BRIGHTRED STUDY GUIDE: NATIONAL 5 PHYSICS

1 ELECTRICITY AND ENERGY

2 WAVES AND RADIATION

3 DYNAMICS AND SPACE

EXAM PRACTICE

GLOSSARY

INTRODUCING NATIONAL 5 PHYSICS

The National 5 Physics course will help you to develop and apply skills for learning, skills for life and skills for work.

Physics is about gaining a knowledge and understanding of how things work, and applying this knowledge to explain and improve the world around us. The skills and knowledge developed by physicists are needed across all sectors of society. As our knowledge and understanding of physics increases, this leads to new technology and improvements in the way that we live in the world.

THE NATIONAL 5 PHYSICS COURSE

The National 5 Physics course encourages you to become:

- a more confident learner
- a responsible citizen with an informed understanding of the impact of technological developments on society resulting from physics, such as the internet, renewable energy and nuclear medicine
- someone who can analyse and understand new information and apply skills to solve problems.

The National 5 Physics course provides opportunities for you to acquire the knowledge and skills relevant to current physics topics. It is designed to help you to understand and investigate the world in an engaging and enjoyable way.

The National 5 Physics course covers many of the major areas of physics. It will give you an insight into the underlying nature of our world and its place in the universe. From the sources of power that we use, to the exploration of space, it covers a range of applications and relationships that have been discovered through experiment and calculation, including those used in modern technology. An experimental and investigative approach is used to develop knowledge and understanding of physics concepts. You will be able to develop a deeper understanding of physics, and describe and interpret physical phenomena using mathematical skills. You will be able to develop scientific methods of research to explore issues in physics and draw conclusions.

The National 5 Physics course has an external assessment and an internal assessment.

THE EXTERNAL ASSESSMENT

The external assessment comes at the end of the course and has two components.

Component 1 – Question Paper (80% of total mark)

This is made up of a two-hour question paper in which:

- 20 marks are allocated to an 'objective test' that contains 20 multiple choice questions
- 90 marks are allocated to the 'written paper' which includes questions requiring a mixture of short (restricted) and extended answers.

Most of the marks will be given for applying knowledge and understanding. The other marks will be awarded for applying scientific enquiry, analytical thinking and problem-solving skills. A Data sheet containing relevant data and formulae will be provided.

The question paper will be written and marked by the Scottish Qualification Authority (SQA).

contd

Component 2 - Assignment (20% of total mark)

The assignment will be an in-depth study of a physics topic you have chosen. There will be 20 marks awarded for the assignment and the majority of these will be awarded for applying scientific enquiry and analytical thinking skills. The other marks will be awarded for applying knowledge and understanding related to the topic.

The assignment is carried out under conditions controlled by your teacher and marked by the SQA. To prepare for the controlled assessment, you will choose, research and investigate an appropriate topic, focusing on the applications and impact on society or the environment.

During the assessment of the assignment you will present evidence of:

- the process you have gone through
- your physics knowledge and understanding relating to the topic
- the application of the topic
- a balanced evaluation of the impact on society or the environment
- a reasoned conclusion.

INTERNAL ASSESSMENT

During your period of study you will be assessed on a range of skills.

Here is the range of skills tested:

- demonstrating knowledge and understanding by making statements, describing information, providing explanations and integrating knowledge
- applying knowledge of physics to new situations, interpreting information and solving problems
- planning, designing and safely carrying out experimental/practical investigations to test given hypotheses or to illustrate particular effects
- selecting information and presenting information appropriately in a variety of forms
- processing information (using calculations and units where appropriate)
- making predictions based on evidence and information
- drawing valid conclusions and giving explanations supported by evidence/justification
- identifying sources of uncertainty and suggesting improvements to experiments/practical investigations
- communicating findings and information.

ONLINE

This book is supported by the BrightRED Digital Zone - head to www.brightredbooks.net/N5Physics for videos, quizzes, games and more!

COURSE CONTENT

The National 5 Physics course consists of three units.

In each unit, you will develop skills of scientific enquiry, investigation and analytical thinking, along with the required knowledge and understanding.

You will also research issues and communicate your findings, while developing skills of scientific literacy.

- Unit 1 - Electricity and energy
- Unit 2 - Waves and radiation
- Unit 3 - Dynamics and space

This book will guide you through the content and skills you need to succeed at National 5 Physics. So, let's get started!

ENERGY AND ELECTRICITY

CONSERVATION OF ENERGY

The key concepts to learn in this topic are:

- the principles of conservation of energy and loss of energy
- energy transfer between stores
- the principle of heat energy (E_h)
- how to perform calculations with gravitational and elastic potential energy (E_p) and kinetic energy (E_k) including situations involving conservation of energy.

VIDEO LINK

Check out the 'Potential and Kinetic Energy' clip at www.brightredbooks.net/N5Physics

ENERGY CONSERVATION AND LOSS

Energy is never destroyed but is always *transformed* (changed) into other *stores* (types) of energy. For example, gravitational potential energy is often transformed into kinetic energy as shown in the diagram of a skateboarder rolling down a hill.

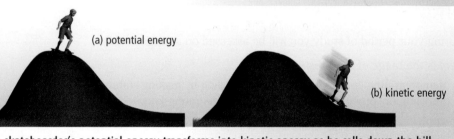

(a) potential energy

(b) kinetic energy

The skateboarder's potential energy transforms into kinetic energy as he rolls down the hill

Heat energy is always produced whenever potential energy is transformed into other stores of energy – whether or not heat energy is wanted. For example, in a car, energy from fuel is transformed by the engine into useful kinetic energy but it is also wasted or lost as heat energy.

A bouncing ball illustrates how energy is transformed.

What happens when the ball is dropped?

As the ball falls, if air resistance is ignored, then all of the gravitational E_p is transformed into E_k.

$E_p \rightarrow E_k$

What happens when the ball stops going up?

When all of the E_k is transformed back into gravitational E_p the ball will be at the top of its bounce – but <u>not</u> at the height it was dropped from because of the E_h that was lost when it changed shape.

What happens when the ball hits the ground?

As the ball hits the ground it changes shape and the E_k transforms into elastic E_p and some E_h.

What happens when the ball rebounds?

As the ball rebounds, the elastic potential energy transforms back into E_k and some E_h and it regains its shape. Then this E_k is transformed into gravitational E_p as the ball gets higher.

Energy transformation in a bouncing ball

Each time the ball bounces, the lost energy means that the ball will rebound to a lower height until eventually it loses all of its energy.

ENERGY CALCULATIONS

To calculate gravitational potential energy use:

$E_p = mgh$

To calculate kinetic energy use:

$E_k = \frac{1}{2}mv^2$

EXAMPLE:

This example illustrates how to calculate speeds, height and lost energy.

(a) A 600 g ball is dropped to the ground from a vertical height of 4 m. Calculate the speed of the ball just as it collides with the ground. Ignore air resistance.

Energy is transformed from potential energy into kinetic energy as the ball falls.

$E_p \rightarrow E_k$ and $mgh = \frac{1}{2}mv^2$

so $v = \sqrt{2gh} = \sqrt{2 \times 9.8 \times 4} = 8.9\,m\,s^{-1}$

(b) When the ball rebounds, it leaves the ground with a speed of 7·4 m s⁻¹. Calculate the height the ball will return to.

This time E_k is transformed into E_p. So $v = \sqrt{2gh}$ rearranges to $h = \dfrac{v^2}{2g}$

$h = \dfrac{7 \cdot 4^2}{2 \times 9 \cdot 8}$

$h = 2 \cdot 8\,m$

(c) Calculate the energy lost when the ball collides with the ground.

Before the collision $\quad E_k = \frac{1}{2}mv^2 = \frac{1}{2} \times 0.6 \times 8.9^2$
$\qquad\qquad\qquad\qquad\quad = 23.8\,J$

After the collision $\qquad E_k = \frac{1}{2}mv^2 = \frac{1}{2} \times 0.6 \times 7.4^2$
$\qquad\qquad\qquad\qquad\quad = 16.4\,J$

Energy lost during collision $\quad = E_k$ before $- E_k$ after collision
$\qquad\qquad\qquad\qquad\quad = 23.8 - 16.4$
$\qquad\qquad\qquad\qquad\quad = 7.4\,J$

ONLINE TEST

Take the 'Conservation of Energy' test at www.brightredbooks.net/N5Physics

DON'T FORGET

Because $E_p \rightarrow E_k$, to determine the final speed at which E_p is transformed into E_k the equation $v = \sqrt{2gh}$ can be used.

DON'T FORGET

To calculate the final rebound height the equation
$h = \dfrac{v^2}{2g}$
can be used.

DON'T FORGET

Remember, 'lost' energy is usually transformed into sound and heat. Sometimes this heat energy can cause the ball to become warm. This is especially noticeable in sports, such as squash and tennis, where there are lots of rebounds.

THINGS TO DO AND THINK ABOUT

Here are some other examples of everyday energy transformations:

The movement of a clock pendulum

Water that is stored in a reservoir and then flows downwards through pipes to a generator in a hydroelectric power station

1. Think of some examples of energy transformations that are going on around you.

2. Consider the energy losses which may occur in these transfers. Why are processes less than 100% efficient in terms of useful energy?

ELECTRICAL CHARGE CARRIERS, ELECTRIC FIELDS AND POTENTIAL DIFFERENCE (VOLTAGE)

The key concepts to learn in this topic are:

- that **electric charge** can be positive or negative
- electric **current** is the *amount* of *charge* carried by a **conductor** every *second*
- how to use $Q = It$, the relationship between charge, current and time
- the difference between **alternating current (a.c.)** and **direct current (d.c.)**
- to understand the effect of an electric field on a charged particle
- that the **potential difference** (or voltage) of the power supply is a measure of the energy given to the charge carriers in a circuit.

DON'T FORGET

Like charges repel, unlike charges attract.

ONLINE TEST

Take the 'Electrical Charge Carriers, Electric Fields and Potential Difference (Voltage)' test at www.brightredbooks.net/N5Physics

ELECTRIC CHARGE

Electrons are negatively charged and protons are positively charged. The diagram shows that, when a plastic rod is rubbed with a duster, the duster gains electrons from the **atoms** of the plastic rod. The plastic rod becomes positively charged because it has lost negatively charged electrons.

The symbol for charge is Q and charge is measured in coulombs (C). When charged particles with the same charge are close to each other, there is a repelling **force** between them. Charged particles with opposite charge attract each other.

Transfer of negative charge from rod to duster

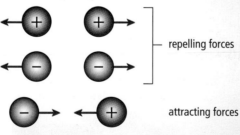

Forces between like and unlike charges

repelling forces

attracting forces

This attraction of unlike charges is used in lots of modern devices, such as photocopiers, laser printers and paint sprayers.

Like charges repel!

ELECTRIC CURRENT

When electrons flow through a conductor, for example a copper wire, an electric current is produced.

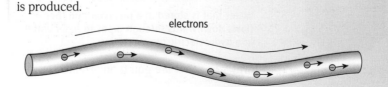

electrons

Electrons in a wire

contd

Current (*I*) is a measure of the amount of charge (*Q*) flowing through a conductor every second (*t*). When a charge of 1 coulomb (1 C) flows through a conductor each second, there is a current of 1 ampere (1 A). Charge is calculated using:

charge = current × time $Q = It$

EXAMPLE:

Calculate how much charge passes through the wire in 4 minutes.

$Q = It$

Remember to convert t into seconds by multiplying by 60.

$Q = 5 × 4 × 60 = 1200\,C$

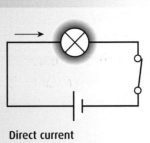

When charge moves constantly in the same direction through a conductor, this is called direct current (d.c.); when charge moves back and forwards through the conductor, this is called alternating current (a.c.).

Direct current

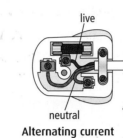

Alternating current

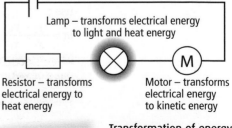

POTENTIAL DIFFERENCE (VOLTAGE)

An electric field is an area where charged particles (such as electrons and protons) experience a force. An electric field can be produced by applying a voltage to two metal plates that are separated by a small gap, as shown in the diagram.

If charged particles are present in the gap, they experience a force and move.

parallel plates

When a **battery** is connected to a wire, this produces an electric field in the wire.

The wire in the diagram is made from metal. The atoms in metals have electrons which are free to move from atom to atom. These electrons are charged particles which experience a force causing them to move through the wire. Each time the electrons move through the battery, it transfers **electrical energy** to them.

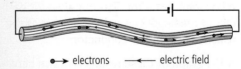

● → electrons   ◄— electric field

Charged particles moving through a wire

Electrons which have received electrical energy from the battery move through wires around the circuit. Work is done each time these electrons pass through a component in the circuit. Some of their energy is transferred to the component. This causes an energy difference across the component, which is known as an electrical **potential difference (p.d.)**

The energy which is required to move the electrons through the component is a measure of the potential difference across the component; it is measured in volts. When 1 joule (1 J) of energy is required to move 1 coulomb (1 C) of charge through a component, the potential difference is 1 joule per coulomb (1 J C⁻¹), or 1 volt (1 V).

The total electrical energy transferred from the battery to the electrons is transferred to the circuit components when they pass through.

Battery – transfers electrical energy to electrons

Lamp – transforms electrical energy to light and heat energy

Resistor – transforms electrical energy to heat energy

Motor – transforms electrical energy to kinetic energy

Transformation of energy within the components of a circuit

THINGS TO DO AND THINK ABOUT

1. Research the variety of uses of electric fields including how electric fields are responsible for accelerating protons to 99·9% of the speed of light in the Large Hadron Collider and how electric fields are used in LCD televisions.

VIDEO LINK

For a closer look at the differences between d.c. and a.c., check out the video at www.brightredbooks.net/N5Physics

DON'T FORGET

Direct current is in one direction only; alternating current changes direction.

VIDEO LINK

To see the effect of an electric field, watch this video at www.brightredbooks.net/N5Physics

DON'T FORGET

Charged particles, such as electrons, protons, **alpha particles**, charged paint droplets and smoke particles, all experience a force in an electric field.

DON'T FORGET

Potential difference or voltage is measured in volts and 1 volt (1 V) is equivalent to 1 joule per coulomb (1 J C⁻¹).

OHM'S LAW

The key concepts to learn in this topic are:

- how to use a *V–I* graph to determine **resistance**
- the use of an appropriate relationship to solve problems involving potential difference (voltage), current and resistance
- the relationship between temperature and resistance for a **conductor**.

AN OVERVIEW OF OHM'S LAW

Resistance is the property of a conductor to oppose current. The larger the resistance in a circuit, the smaller the current. Resistance can be calculated using the relationship:

$$R = \frac{V}{I}$$

Where: R is the resistance in ohms (Ω)

V is the potential differences (voltage) in volts (V)

I is the current in amperes (A)

This is Ohm's Law.

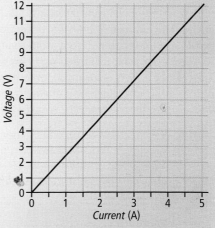

Resistors

An experiment to explore Ohm's Law

An experiment using the apparatus in Circuit 1 can be used to verify Ohm's Law for a conductor. The current in the circuit is changed by adjusting the variable resistor.

Voltage and current readings are recorded in a table like the one shown below, to the left.

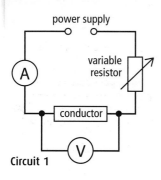

Circuit 1

Voltage (V)	Current (A)	$\frac{V}{I}$
3·0	1·25	2·4
6·0	2·5	2·4
9·0	3·75	2·4
12·0	5·0	2·4

The third column in the table gives the results of a calculation of $\frac{V}{I}$ for each pair of *V–I* values.

A constant value for $\frac{V}{I}$ is obtained for each pair of readings. This value is known as the resistance, R, of the conductor.

A *V–I* graph of these results is drawn here.

This straight line graph which passes through the origin shows that the current is directly proportional to the voltage (the graphs shows a linear relationship). This means that if voltage is doubled, current is doubled, and so on.

The *gradient* of this graph will determine the ratio $\frac{V}{I}$.

To calculate the gradient of the *V–I* graph, use :

$$m = \frac{y_2 - y_1}{x_2 - x_1}$$ where m is the gradient.

Choose values for (x_2, y_2) and (x_1, y_1) from the graph. (Hint: choose pairs of values which are easy to read from the graph!)

Choosing: $(x_2, y_2) \rightarrow (5\cdot0, 12\cdot0)$ and $(x_1, y_1) \rightarrow (1\cdot5, 3\cdot6)$

$$m = \frac{y_2 - y_1}{x_2 - x_1} = \frac{12\cdot0 - 3\cdot6}{5\cdot0 - 1\cdot5} = \frac{8\cdot4}{3\cdot5} = 2\cdot4$$

The gradient is the resistance, R, of the conductor, so $R = 2\cdot4\,\Omega$.

The results and graph obtained from this experiment confirm the relationship between voltage V, current I and resistance R: $R = \frac{V}{I}$

A graph of *V–I* can be used to prove Ohm's Law

contd

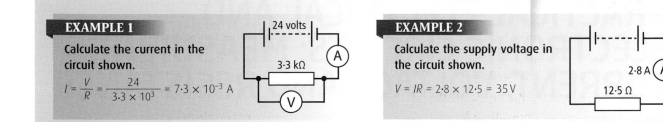

EXAMPLE 1

Calculate the current in the
circuit shown.

$I = \dfrac{V}{R} = \dfrac{24}{3\cdot3 \times 10^3} = 7\cdot3 \times 10^{-3}$ A

24 volts

3·3 kΩ

EXAMPLE 2

Calculate the supply voltage in
the circuit shown.

$V = IR = 2\cdot8 \times 12\cdot5 = 35$ V

2·8 A

12·5 Ω

RESISTANCE AND TEMPERATURE CHANGE

The resistance of a conductor remains constant as long as its temperature remains
constant. Materials which have a linear relationship between the applied voltage and
current are said to be *ohmic conductors*. Conductors made from carbon or metals are
ohmic over a range of current values.

NON-OHMIC CONDUCTORS

For some materials, a change in temperature can cause a change in resistance.

Materials which have a non-linear relationship between the applied voltage and
current are said to be *non-ohmic conductors*. The shape of the *V–I* graph for non-ohmic
conductors is not a straight line.

For non-ohmic conductors, the value of resistance cannot be found by calculating
the gradient of a voltage–current graph. It has to be calculated using Ohm's Law with
specific voltage and current values taken from the graph or table of results. Non-ohmic
conductors do not have a fixed resistance when the current in the conductor changes.

Examples of non-ohmic components

A filament lamp

When a **filament lamp** is investigated using the circuit shown in the diagram this
voltage–current graph is obtained.

The graph is not a straight line, which means that the resistance of the filament wire is
not constant for different current values. As the current increases, the filament heats up,
and the resistance *increases*.

A thermistor

When a thermistor is investigated using the circuit in the diagram this voltage–current
graph is obtained.

The graph is not a straight line, which means that the resistance of the thermistor is not
constant for different values of current. As the current increases the resistance of the
thermistor *decreases*.

EXAMPLE 3

Use the following *V–I* graph of a thermistor
to calculate its resistance when the current
is 2 A, 5 A and 8 A.

2 A: $R = \dfrac{V}{I} = \dfrac{10}{2} = 5\,\Omega$ 5 A: $R = \dfrac{V}{I} = \dfrac{16}{5} = 3\cdot2\,\Omega$

8 A: $R = \dfrac{V}{I} = \dfrac{21}{8} = 2\cdot6\,\Omega$

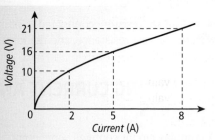

THINGS TO DO AND THINK ABOUT

1. Investigate the properties of a **diode** and find out how its resistance changes when
different voltages are applied to it.

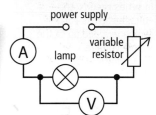

Filament lamp investigation

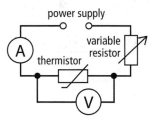

Voltage–current graph for
filament lamp

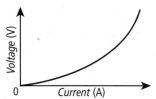

Thermistor investigation

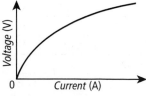

Voltage–current graph for
thermistor

DON'T FORGET

If the V–I graph for the
component is not straight
and through the origin,
then the resistance of the
component is not a fixed
value.

PRACTICAL ELECTRICAL AND ELECTRONIC CIRCUITS: MEASURING CURRENT, VOLTAGE AND RESISTANCE

The key concepts to learn in this topic are:

- the measurement of current, voltage and resistance using appropriate meters in series, parallel and complex circuits
- current and voltage relationships in series and parallel circuits.

DON'T FORGET

In series circuits, the voltages across each component add up to the supply voltage.

MEASURING CURRENT AND VOLTAGE IN SERIES CIRCUITS

In a series circuit, the *same current* passes through each component.

In a series circuit, the supply *voltage divides* across each component.

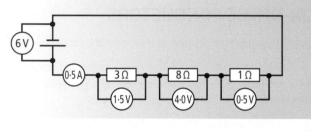

Current and voltage in components in series

VIDEO LINK

To see the differences between series and parallel circuits in practice, watch the video at www.brightredbooks.net/N5Physics

MEASURING CURRENT AND VOLTAGE IN PARALLEL CIRCUITS

- In a parallel circuit, the supply *current splits up* through each component when it reaches a branch in the circuit.

- In a parallel circuit, the *voltage* across components connected in parallel *remains the same as the supply voltage*.

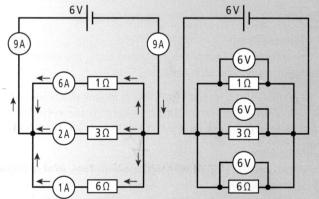

Current and voltage in components in parallel

In the circuits above, the 9 A supply current splits up through each branch of the circuit.

The supply voltage of 6 V appears across each resistor connected in parallel.

Note that for resistors connected in parallel, the smallest current is present in the branch with the largest resistance, and the largest current is present in the smallest resistance.

MEASURING CURRENT AND VOLTAGE IN COMPLEX CIRCUITS

A complex circuit contains some components that are connected in series and some that are connected in parallel. Care is required to determine the current and voltage at different positions in the circuit.

Current in a complex circuit

The circuit in the diagram consists of parts where resistors are connected in series, and parts where they are connected in parallel. To determine the current at different

contd

positions in the complex circuit, it is important to trace the path of current from the supply through the circuit and back to the supply.

- In the circuit, the total current of 1 A leaves and enters the supply.

- The total current of 1 A is present in the 1 Ω and 9 Ω resistor because they are connected in series with the supply. This is shown on the **ammeters** which are displaying the total current.

- The 4 Ω resistors are connected in parallel. The total current of 1 A divides equally between them – 0·5 A and 0·5 A. This is displayed on the ammeters in the parallel part of the circuit.

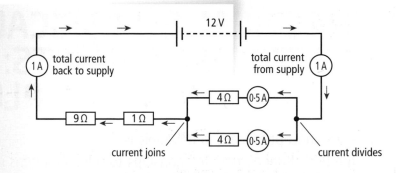

Current in a complex circuit

Voltage in a complex circuit

To determine the voltage across components in a complex circuit, it is important to recognise the parts of the circuit where components are connected in series, and the parts that are connected in parallel.

In the circuit in the diagram the supply voltage will be distributed across the components.

Using voltmeters to display the voltage across different components shows that the voltage divides where there are components in series – across the 9 Ω and 1 Ω resistors. Components that are connected in parallel have the *same* voltage across both resistors.

Work out which parts of the circuit are in parallel and which parts are in series

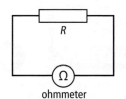

DON'T FORGET

In complex circuits, current has the same value as the supply in the series parts, but divides in the parallel parts.

ONLINE TEST

Take the 'Practical Electrical and Electronic Circuits: Measuring Current, Voltage and Resistance' test at www.brightredbooks.net/N5Physics

MEASUREMENT OF RESISTANCE

There are two ways to measure the resistance of a component in a circuit.

Method 1 – remove component from the circuit and connect to an ohmmeter
For example, in the circuit shown above, if the 4 Ω resistance was unknown and had to be determined, we would disconnect the resistor and connect it to an ohmmeter as shown here.

ohmmeter

Measured value for $R = 4\,\Omega$

Method 2 – use an ammeter and voltmeter, and a calculation
With the component connected in a circuit, an ammeter and voltmeter can be used to measure the current in it and the voltage across it. Then a calculation is carried out.

For example, we could connect the resistor to a supply, as shown in the diagram, and obtain current and voltmeter readings. Then we would use Ohm's Law to calculate the resistance.

$$R = \frac{V}{I} = \frac{2}{0.5} = 4\,\Omega$$

When using this method, it is good practice to repeat the resistance calculation for different readings of current and voltage, and to calculate the *average* value for R.

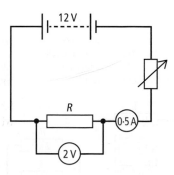

THINGS TO DO AND THINK ABOUT

1. When measuring current, voltage and resistance using a multimeter, it is important to adjust the multimeter for the appropriate measurement of I, V or R. Find out how to select the appropriate settings on a multimeter to measure current, voltage and resistance, and how to make sure that the correct *range* is selected for the measurement.

PRACTICAL ELECTRICAL AND ELECTRONIC CIRCUITS: SERIES, PARALLEL AND COMPLEX CIRCUITS

The key concept to learn in this topic is:

- the use of appropriate relationships to solve problems involving the total resistance of resistors in series and in parallel circuits, and circuits with a combination of series and parallel resistors.

Electrical circuits can have resistors connected in series, or in parallel. More complex circuits have combinations of resistors connected in both series and in parallel.

DON'T FORGET

When the total *resistance* of a circuit *increases*, the supply current *decreases*.

ohmmeter

DON'T FORGET

When the resistance values have mixed units (like ohms Ω and kilohms kΩ) they must be converted into ohms before using the relationship.

VIDEO LINK

Check out the tutorial for more on resistors in series at www.brightredbooks.net/N5Physics

DON'T FORGET

The combined resistance of resistors in parallel is always less than the resistance of the smallest resistor.

ohmmeter

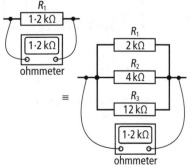

ohmmeter

Working out the combined resistance of resistors in parallel

RESISTORS IN SERIES CIRCUITS

When resistors are connected in *series*, the total resistance of the circuit *increases*.

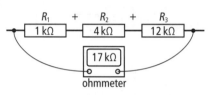

Resistors connected in series

One single resistor can replace several resistors connected in series.

For example, a single resistor of value $17\,k\Omega$ can replace three resistors of values $1\,k\Omega$, $4\,k\Omega$ and $12\,k\Omega$ which are connected in series in a circuit.

Add to get the sum of resistors in a series circuit.

The combined resistance of resistors connected in series can be found using the relationship $R_T = R_1 + R_2 + ...$:

EXAMPLE 1

Calculate the total resistance in circuit in the diagram.

$R_T = R_1 + R_2 + R_3$
$\quad = 1\cdot2 \times 10^3 + 250 + 15 \times 10^3 = 16450\,\Omega$

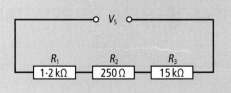

RESISTORS IN PARALLEL CIRCUITS

When more resistors are connected in parallel, the total resistance of the circuit *decreases*.

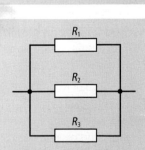

Resistors connected in parallel

One single resistor can replace several resistors connected in parallel in a circuit. For example, a single resistor of value $1\cdot2\,k\Omega$ can replace three resistors of value $2\,k\Omega$, $4\,k\Omega$ and $12\,k\Omega$ that are connected in parallel in a circuit.

The combined resistance of resistors connected in parallel can be found using the relationship: $\dfrac{1}{R_T} = \dfrac{1}{R_1} + \dfrac{1}{R_2} + ...$

EXAMPLE 2

Calculate the combined resistance in the circuit in the diagram.

$\dfrac{1}{R_T} = \dfrac{1}{R_1} + \dfrac{1}{R_2} + ...$

$\dfrac{1}{R_T} = \dfrac{1}{R_1} + \dfrac{1}{R_2} + \dfrac{1}{R_3}$ Use this relationship to calculate the answer.

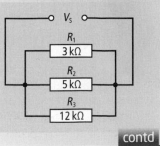

contd

$$= \frac{1}{3} + \frac{1}{5} + \frac{1}{12}$$ Write out the fractions.

$= 0.333 + 0.2 + 0.083 = 0.616$ Calculate the fractions (usually to three decimal places).

$$R_T = \frac{1}{0.616}$$ Calculate 1 divided by this intermediate answer

$= 1.62 k\Omega$ to get the final answer.

Since all resistance values in the example are given in kilohms, there is no need to convert into ohms. The units for the final answer will be kilohms.

When resistors connected in parallel have the same resistance values, there is a shortcut to calculate the combined resistance instead of using the relationship. The combined resistance of three identical resistors is $\frac{1}{3}$ of the single resistance. If there are two identical resistors, their combined resistance is $\frac{1}{2}$ of the single resistance.

EXAMPLE 3

Use the shortcut to calculate the combined resistance of the resistors in the circuit.

Total number of resistors = 3

Total resistance = $\frac{1}{3}$ of one resistance = $\frac{12}{3}$ $R_T = 4\Omega$

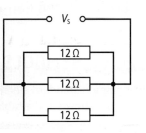

RESISTORS IN COMPLEX CIRCUITS

Complex circuits have combinations of resistors connected in both series parts and parallel, as shown in the diagram.

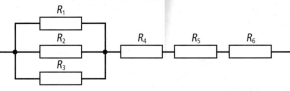

Complex combination of resistors

When circuits contain a mixture of resistors connected in series and in parallel, to calculate the total resistance, both relationships

$R_T = R_1 + R_2 \ldots$ and $\frac{1}{R_T} = \frac{1}{R_1} + \frac{1}{R_2} + \ldots$ have to be applied separately.

EXAMPLE 4

Calculate the total resistance in this circuit between points X and Y.

Part of the circuit has resistors connected in series, and part has resistors connected in parallel. It is important to separate the two parts.

To find the combined resistance of the circuit, the total resistance of each part must be calculated separately.

Part 1: $R_T = 17 k\Omega$ (See Example of resistors connected in series.)

Part 2: $R_T = 1.62 k\Omega$ (See Example 2 for calculation of resistors connected in parallel.)

Since Part 1 and Part 2 are in series, the final *total* resistance is the sum of these two resistance values.

$R_T = R_1 + R_2 = 17 + 1.62 = 18.62 \ k\Omega$

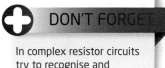

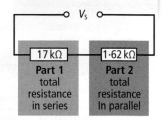

Work out which resistors are in series and which are in parallel

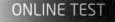

Part 1 of the circuit is in series with part 2

THINGS TO DO AND THINK ABOUT

1. Use resistors of known values to construct series, parallel and complex mixed (series and parallel) circuits. Calculate R_T, then check your answer using an ohmmeter.

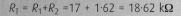

PRACTICAL ELECTRICAL AND ELECTRONIC CIRCUITS: STANDARD ELECTRICAL COMPONENTS 1

The key concepts to learn in this topic are:

- knowledge of the circuit symbol and how to explain the function and application of standard electrical and electronic components including cell, battery, lamp, switch, resistor, variable resistor, voltmeter, ammeter, LED, motor, microphone, loudspeaker, photovoltaic cell, fuse, diode, capacitor, thermistor, LDR, relay, transistor (npn transistor and n-channel enhancement mode MOSFET)
- how to explain the function of an npn transistor or MOSFET transistor as a switch in transistor switching circuits.

DON'T FORGET

You could be asked to draw these symbols in the exam.

CIRCUIT SYMBOLS

The common standard electrical and electronic components and symbols used in this course are shown in the table.

Component	Property	Function	Symbol
Cell	A store of *chemical energy* which transforms into electrical energy	Provides electrical energy to make charge move in a circuit	
Battery	A store of chemical energy which transforms into electrical energy	Provides electrical energy to make charge move in a circuit	
Photovoltaic cell (solar cell)	Transforms *light energy* into electrical energy	A renewable energy source, these cells can be used to provide electrical energy to recharge batteries for portable electronic appliances and, for example, vehicle speed warning signs	solar cell
Variable resistor	Opposes the movement of charge in a circuit	Used to vary the size of current	
Voltmeter	Measures voltage in circuits	Measures the voltage across components	V
Ammeter	Measures current in circuits	Measures the current in components	A
Fuse	Device which contains a wire with a low melting point which heats up and melts if current exceeds a given value	The fuse melts and breaks the circuit if the current in the circuit increases above the set fuse value	
Diode	Electronic device which allows current in one direction only	Used in electronic circuits	
LED (light emitting diode)	Electronic device which allows current in one direction only, emits light, and uses low values of current	Used as an indicator and for low energy lighting, e.g. car brakelights and sidelights	
Capacitor	Stores charge	Used in electronic amplifiers and timing circuits	
LDR (light dependent resistor)	Electronic device with changing resistance depending on the light level	Used in circuits to detect and control light levels	
Thermistor	Electronic device with changing resistance depending on its temperature	Used in circuits to detect and control temperature	
Motor	Transforms electrical energy into kinetic energy	Motor speed depends on size of the supply voltage and its direction can be reversed	M
Loudspeaker	Transforms electrical energy signals into *sound energy*	Converts output from amplifiers into sounds	
Microphone	Transforms sound energy signals into electrical energy	Converts sound energy into electrical signals for amplifiers	
Relay	Acts as a remote switch to switch on a separate circuit	When current is present in the relay coil, a switch in a separate circuit is closed	coil
Transistor	Semiconductor device which acts as an electronic switch or amplifier	Used in electronic switching circuits and amplifiers	bipolar transistor MOSFET*

(*metal oxide semiconductor field-effect transistor)

VOLTAGE DIVIDER CIRCUITS

Whenever components are used in circuits and are connected to a battery, they can be connected in series with one or more resistors, in a circuit known as a *voltage divider circuit*.

The battery voltage divides between the resistor and the component. This is to control the voltage across the component – sometimes to protect it from damage and sometimes to be able to monitor how the voltage across the component changes.

A simple voltage divider circuit consists of two resistors in series connected to a supply. The resistor with the greatest resistance has the greatest share of the supply voltage across it. The voltages across the components add up to the supply voltage.

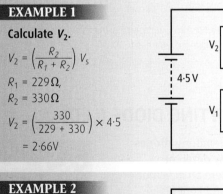

Voltage divider circuit   LED circuit   LDR circuit   Thermistor circuit

Examples of voltage divider circuits

Voltage divider circuit

CALCULATING VOLTAGE OR RESISTANCE IN VOLTAGE DIVIDER CIRCUITS

When calculating values of voltage or resistance in these circuits, there are *two* relationships which can be used, depending on the information given in the circuit.

Method 1

When the supply voltage and both resistor values are given, and either V_1 or V_2 has to be calculated, this relationship is used:

$$V_2 = \left(\frac{R_2}{R_1 + R_2}\right) V_S$$

EXAMPLE 1

Calculate V_2.

$V_2 = \left(\frac{R_2}{R_1 + R_2}\right) V_S$

$R_1 = 229\,\Omega$,
$R_2 = 330\,\Omega$

$V_2 = \left(\frac{330}{229 + 330}\right) \times 4{\cdot}5$

$= 2{\cdot}66\text{V}$

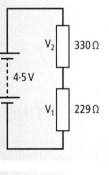

V_2 $330\,\Omega$

$4{\cdot}5\,\text{V}$

V_1 $229\,\Omega$

Method 2

This relationship is used when the supply voltage is not given, but the voltage across a resistor or a resistor value has to be calculated:

$$\frac{V_1}{V_2} = \frac{R_1}{R_2}$$

EXAMPLE 2

Calculate the value of R_2.

$\frac{V_1}{V_2} = \frac{R_1}{R_2}$

$V_1 = 8{\cdot}9\text{V},\ V_2 = 3{\cdot}2\text{V}$

$\frac{8{\cdot}9}{3{\cdot}2} = \frac{420}{R_2}$

$R_2 = 420 \times \frac{3{\cdot}2}{8{\cdot}9}$

$= 151\,\Omega$

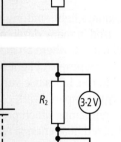

R_2 (3·2V)

$420\,\Omega$ (8·9V)

THINGS TO DO AND THINK ABOUT

1. Connect a circuit for Method 1, where the values of R_1 and R_2 and the supply voltage V_s are known. Use the relationship to calculate a value for the voltage across R_2. Measure the value and compare it with the calculated value.

2. Connect a circuit for Method 2, using known resistors for R_1 and R_2. Measure voltage V_1 using a voltmeter. Use the relationship to calculate a value for voltage V_2. Measure the value and compare it with the calculated value.

PRACTICAL ELECTRICAL AND ELECTRONIC CIRCUITS: STANDARD ELECTRICAL COMPONENTS 2

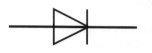

A diode symbol

DIODES

Diodes are electronic devices which are used in circuits to control the direction of current. Diodes only conduct if they are connected the correct way round in a circuit, as shown in the diagram.

If you think of the diode symbol as looking like an arrowhead, then, for the diode (and circuit) to conduct, it should point towards the negative terminal of the supply.

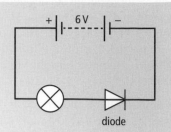

When connected in this way, the diode would conduct and the lamp would light

EXAMPLE: 1

In this circuit, explain which lamps would light.

The diode connected to A is pointing the wrong way, so will not conduct – lamp A will be off.

Although one diode connected to B is pointing the correct way, the other diode is in series with it and is pointing the wrong way, so it will not conduct – lamp B will be off.

The diode connected to C is pointing the correct way and will conduct, so lamp C will light.

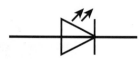

The symbol for a light emitting diode

LIGHT EMITTING DIODE (LED)

Nowadays light emitting **diodes** are used in many different applications where an indicator light or a powerful light beam is required. LEDs use very little energy compared with conventional filament lamps which produce a lot of wasted heat energy. Also, LEDs have a longer life.

An LED Screen TV

They are low voltage devices and commonly operate at a voltage of around 2 V and a current of around 20–200 mA. When used with a supply of more than 2 V, they are connected in series with a resistor, R, in a voltage divider circuit. This protects the LED from damage due to too large a voltage or current.

Remember, LEDs are diodes and only conduct if they are connected in circuits in the correct orientation.

When calculating the resistance of the resistor which protects the LED, information such as the operating current and voltage of the LED will be provided.

contd

EXAMPLE 2

Calculate the resistance of *R* that allows the LED to operate at the correct voltage and current.

First calculate the voltage across resistor *R*.

$V_R = V_S - V_{LED} = 4.5 - 1.8 = 2.7\,V$

Then use Ohm's Law to calculate the resistance of *R*.

$R = \dfrac{V}{I} = \dfrac{2.7}{15 \times 10^{-3}} = 180\,\Omega$

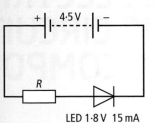

LED 1·8 V 15 mA

DON'T FORGET

Work out the voltage across the resistor first, before using Ohm's Law.

TRANSISTORS

Transistors are electronic components that feature in many electrical devices including computers, televisions and mobile phones. Sometimes they are discrete components, like the ones shown in the picture, but often hundreds are contained in a single microchip.

- A transistor is a semiconductor device which can be used as a switch.

- Two of the main types of transistor are the bipolar transistor and the MOSFET.

Bipolar transistor

MOSFET transistor

Transistors

When used in a switch circuit, the transistor is off (non-conducting) until its input voltage is greater than 0·7 V (for a bipolar transistor) or 2 V (for a MOSFET transistor), at which point the transistor switches on (starts conducting).

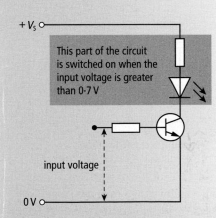

$+V_S$

This part of the circuit is switched on when the input voltage is greater than 0·7 V

input voltage

0 V

Bipolar transistor switching circuit

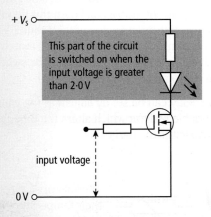

$+V_S$

This part of the circuit is switched on when the input voltage is greater than 2·0 V

input voltage

0 V

MOSFET transistor switching circuit

VIDEO LINK

For more on the uses of transistors, watch the video at www.brightredbooks.net/N5Physics

DON'T FORGET

The transistor will switch on a device, or even a separate circuit, when its input voltage is above a given value.

Transistors are used to switch different devices on (or off) when their input voltage changes above (or below) the switching voltage. This changing voltage is often provided by a voltage divider circuit. The change in voltage can be caused by a variety of different conditions, such as a change in light level or temperature.

THINGS TO DO AND THINK ABOUT

1. Find out how the use of LEDs as light sources has reduced the energy bills in homes and in industry.

2. Find out how transistors are used as building blocks in the microchips of all electronic devices from computers to mobile phones.

PRACTICAL ELECTRICAL AND ELECTRONIC CIRCUITS: STANDARD ELECTRICAL COMPONENTS 3

Electrolytic capacitor

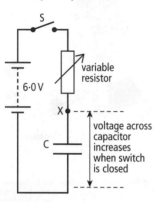

Circuit 1 – the voltage across a capacitor increases as more charge is stored

The greater the capacitance or resistance in a capacitor circuit, the longer the charging time.

Test your knowledge of the uses of electrical and electronic components in circuits online, at www.brightredbooks.net/N5Physics

CAPACITORS

Capacitors are components which store charge.

Symbol for a capacitor

In Circuit 1, when switch S is closed, the capacitor begins to store charge. The voltage across the capacitor increases. The voltage at position X increases.

Facts about capacitors:

1. The capacitor becomes fully charged when the voltage across it gradually increases to reach the supply voltage.
2. At this point, the current in the circuit reduces to zero.
3. When a capacitor discharges, the voltage across it gradually decreases and reaches zero.
4. The length of time a capacitor takes to charge depends upon the capacitance of the capacitor and the resistance of the resistor in series with it. The greater the value of the capacitance or resistance, the longer the capacitor takes to charge up.
5. The unit for capacitance is the farad (F).
6. Typical values for capacitors are: 22 microfarads (22×10^{-6} F or $22\,\mu$F) or 15 picofarads (15×10^{-12} F or 15 pF).

Capacitors are often used in timing circuits.

When the capacitor-charging part of Circuit 2 is connected to a transistor circuit, the voltage across the capacitor at position X becomes the input voltage to the transistor. When this voltage reaches the appropriate value of 0·7 V (but 2 V for a MOSFET transistor) the transistor will switch on (or conduct). In this circuit, the transistor switches on a buzzer, to make a countdown timer.

The time delay can be set by adjusting the value of the variable resistor which alters the time taken for the capacitor to charge.

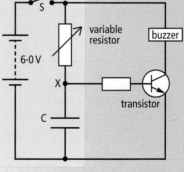

Circuit 2 – capacitor timer

THERMISTORS

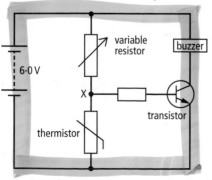

Symbol for a thermistor

Thermistors are resistors which change their resistance as their temperature changes. Most thermistors are designed to have a decrease in resistance as the temperature rises.

Circuit 3 opposite is used to switch on a warning buzzer whenever the temperature falls below a certain value.

When the temperature falls, the thermistor's resistance increases and so it gains a bigger share of the supply voltage. The voltage across the thermistor will eventually become bigger than 0·7 V at position X, causing the transistor to switch on and the buzzer to sound.

The resistance of the variable resistor can be adjusted, which changes the thermistor resistance required to switch on the transistor – giving a different switching temperature.

Circuit 3 – low-temperature warning circuit

LIGHT DEPENDENT RESISTOR (LDR)

Light dependent resistors are devices which change their resistance as the light level changes; the resistance of LDRs decreases as the light level increases.

The symbol for an LDR

This light dependent resistor circuit shown here is used to switch on a high intensity LED whenever the daylight level falls below a fixed value.

When the light level falls, the LDR's resistance increases and it gains a bigger share of the supply voltage. The voltage across the LDR will eventually become bigger than 0·7 V, and the transistor will switch on and the LED will light.

The resistance of the variable resistor can be adjusted which will change the LDR resistance required to switch on the transistor – giving a different switching light level.

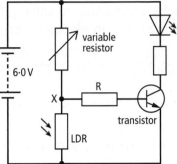
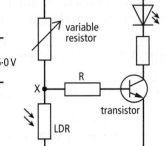

Light dependent resistor circuit

VIDEO LINK

Have a look at the LDR circuit clip at www.brightredbooks.net/N5Physics

DON'T FORGET

This might help you remember how the resistance changes with temperature or light level:
• Temperature Up-Resistance Down (TURD)
• Light Up-Resistance Down (LURD)!

SOLAR CELL (PHOTOVOLTAIC CELL)

A solar cell transforms light energy into electrical energy. A voltage is produced when light shines on a solar cell.

solar cell

Symbol for a solar cell

Solar cells are commonly used to recharge batteries in portable or remote appliances (for example, your calculator might have a solar cell to recharge an internal battery).

EXAMPLE:

High intensity LEDs are used as path lights. The lights turn on automatically when it gets dark. The light contains a solar cell which charges a rechargeable battery during daylight hours. When dark, at night, the rechargeable batteries provide energy for the LEDs to light up the path.

At a particular daylight level, the voltage across the 400 Ω resistor is 0·4 V.

(a) Calculate the voltage across the rechargeable battery at this light level.

$$\frac{V_1}{V_2} = \frac{R_1}{R_2}$$

$$\frac{0·4}{V_2} = \frac{400}{1200}$$

$$V_2 = \frac{0·4 \times 1200}{400} = 1·2V$$

(b) Calculate the voltage generated by the solar cell.

$$V_{solar\ cell} = V_1 + V_2 = 0·4 + 1·2 = 1·6V$$

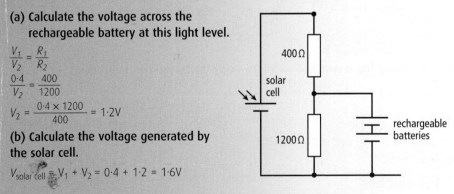

The solar cell and rechargeable batteries are part of the circuit shown here.

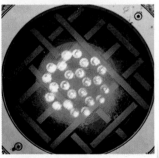

This house has a bank of solar cells on the roof

A sunken LED light

DON'T FORGET

The greater the light intensity, the greater the voltage generated from the solar cell.

THINGS TO DO AND THINK ABOUT

1. Find some other applications which use capacitors in timing circuits.

2. Think of applications where LDRs and thermistors are used in control circuits for lighting and temperature control.

3. Find out how solar cells are being fitted to houses to help reduce electricity bills, and reduce the amount of electrical energy required from burning fossil fuels in Scotland.

ELECTRICAL POWER

The key concepts you will learn in this topic are:

- the use of an appropriate relationship to solve problems involving energy, power and time
- the use of an appropriate relationship to solve problems involving power, potential difference (voltage), current and resistance in electrical circuits
- the selection of an appropriate fuse rating given the power rating of an electrical appliance. (3 A fuse for most appliances rated up to 720 W, 13 A fuse for appliances rated over 720 W.)

VAC

Model: V-015T

220–240 V - 50 Hz
1600 W

Serial number:
01463/33   Made in China

Appliance rating plates tell you the power rating

POWER

When energy is transferred from one store to another, for example when water stored behind a dam (E_p) flows down pipes (E_k) to a river below, it takes time for the energy to transfer.

Whenever there is a current in a circuit, electrical energy is transferred. The electrical energy can be transferred into light (by a lamp), or heat (by a heater), or kinetic energy (by a motor) depending on the appliance in the circuit.

The rate at which energy is transferred is known as *power*. Power is measured in joules per second, or watts (W).

Power can be calculated in a number of ways:

1. $P = \dfrac{E}{t}$ where:

   P is the power in watts (W)
   E is the energy in joules (J)
   t is the time in seconds (s)

2. $P = IV$ where:

   P is the power in watts (W)
   I is the current in amperes (A)
   V is the voltage in volts (V)

3. $P = I^2R$ where:

   P is the power in watts (W)
   I is the current in amperes (A)
   R is the resistance in ohms (Ω)

4. $P = \dfrac{V^2}{R}$ where:

   P is the power in watts (W)
   V is the voltage in volts (V)
   R is the resitatnce in ohms (Ω)

EXAMPLE 1

A 3 kW electric fire is switched on for 2½ hours. Calculate the energy used.

$P = \dfrac{E}{t}$ (convert 2½ hours into seconds)

$3000 = \dfrac{E}{2\cdot5 \times 60 \times 60}$

$E = 3000 \times 2\cdot5 \times 60 \times 60 = 27\,000\,000\,J$

EXAMPLE 2

A 3 kW electric fire is switched on for 2½ hours. Calculate the number of kilowatt-hours (kWh) used.

Kilowatt-hours are an alternative unit for energy, often used by power companies. To calculate kilowatt-hours, use the same formula but keep the units for power and time in kilowatts and hours.

$P = \dfrac{E}{t}$ so $3 = \dfrac{E}{2\cdot5}$

$E = 3 \times 2\cdot5 = 7\cdot5\,kWh$

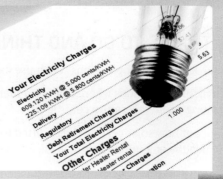

contd

EXAMPLE 3

Calculate the power rating of a 3·2 V ultra-bright LED which has an operating current of 30 mA.

$P = IV = 30 \times 10^{-3} \times 3·2 = 0·01\,\text{W}$

EXAMPLE 4

In a 250 km length of overhead power cable, the power loss due to the heating effect of current in the wires is 14 MW. The current in the cables is 900 A. Calculate the resistance of the cables.

$P = I^2R$

$14 \times 10^6 = 900^2 \times R$

$R = \dfrac{14 \times 10^6}{900^2} = 17·3\,\Omega$

EXAMPLE 5

Calculate the potential difference across the cable in Example 4.

$P = IV$

$14 \times 10^6 = 900 \times V$

$V = \dfrac{14 \times 10^6}{900} = 1·6 \times 10^4\,\text{V}$

EXAMPLE 6

A 1·2 kW mains-operated hairdryer has a current of 0·04 A when blowing cold air only. Calculate the resistance of the heating element.

Power of motor only (cold air)

$P = IV = 0·04 \times 230 = 9·2\,\text{W}$

1·2 kW = 1200 W This is the total power of the hairdryer when both motor and heater are working.

Power of heating element only = 1200 – 9·2 = 1190·8 W

Note that, since the appliance is mains operated V = 230 V

$P = \dfrac{V^2}{R}$

$1190·8 = \dfrac{230^2}{R}$

$R = \dfrac{230^2}{1190·8} = 44·4\,\Omega$

DON'T FORGET

Mains-operated appliances operate at 230 V.

VIDEO LINK

For more on electrical power, watch the video online at www.brightredbooks.net/N5Physics

ONLINE TEST

Test yourself on electrical power online at www.brightredbooks.net/N5Physics

FUSE RATINGS

The current rating (e.g. 3A or 13A) of fuses in plugs of domestic appliances is determined by the Power Rating of the appliance.

For most appliances with a power rating up to 720 W a 3 A fuse should be used.
For appliances with a power rating greater than 720 W a 13 A fuse should be used.

THINGS TO DO AND THINK ABOUT

1. Find out how householders can reduce their electrical power consumption.

2. Think about the electrical appliances in your house which are left on standby when not in use.

3. Compare the power and running cost of domestic appliances when, for 5 hours, they are:

   a) left switched on   b) left on standby   c) switched off.

4. Find out about energy saving by use of these renewable energy sources:

   • solar cells   • heat pumps   • wind turbines.

SPECIFIC HEAT CAPACITY 1

The key concepts to learn in this topic are:

- that different materials require different quantities of heat to raise the temperature of unit mass by one degree Celsius
- that the temperature of a substance is a measure of the mean kinetic energy of its particles
- an explanation of the connection between temperature and heat energy
- the use of an appropriate relationship to solve problems involving mass, heat energy, temperature change and specific heat capacity
- the use of the principle of conservation of energy to determine heat transfer

VIDEO LINK

Head online and watch the video of a hot iron bar and see how different the particles look when heated at www.brightredbooks.net/N5Physics

DON'T FORGET

When substances are heated and their temperature rises, this is because the average kinetic energy of all the particles in the substance has increased.

Far more heat energy is required to heat a bath full of water to body temperature than is needed to heat water for a cup of tea to a far higher temperature.

DON'T FORGET

The change in temperature for a material is written as ΔT where the symbol Δ (pronounced 'delta') stands for the change in temperature of the material.

DON'T FORGET

1 kg of copper will heat up at a different rate than 1 kg of water.

ATOMS, MOLECULES AND ENERGY

The **atoms** and **molecules** which make up every substance are continually moving at different **speeds** and with different kinetic energies. The temperature of a substance is proportional to the average value of these kinetic energies.

When heat energy is transferred to these atoms and molecules, they gain more kinetic energy.

When a substance is heated and its temperature rises, this is because the average value of the kinetic energy of all of the atoms or molecules has increased.

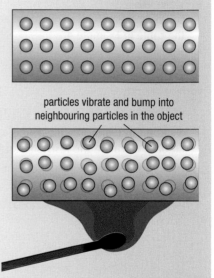

particles vibrate and bump into neighbouring particles in the object

The effect of heating on the particles in an object

TEMPERATURE CHANGE AND HEAT ENERGY

To be able to determine accurately the amount of heat energy required to change the temperature of different materials a detailed study is needed.

When heat energy is added to or removed from a material, causing its temperature to rise or fall, the *change* in temperature depends on:

- the type of material
- the mass of the material
- the amount of heat energy added or removed.

The effect of changing each of these quantities is shown in the following experiments.

Experiment 1 – heating different materials

In the following experiment, equal masses of aluminium, water and iron were given the same amount of heat energy and the temperature change (ΔT) was recorded in each case. The results are shown in the table.

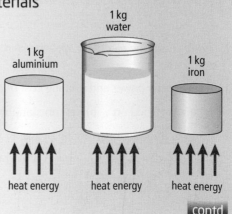

Material	Heat energy added (J)	Temperature change ΔT (°C)
aluminium	37 500	42
water	37 500	9
iron	37 500	78

contd

The results show that when the same amount of heat energy is added to, or removed from, the same mass of different materials, the temperature change is different. The temperature change, ΔT, depends on a quantity called the specific heat capacity for the material (given the symbol, c).

The units for specific heat capacity are $J\,kg^{-1}\,°C^{-1}$.

Experiment 2 - adding different amounts of heat energy to equal masses of the same material

The same mass of water is heated in identical beakers. Different amounts of heat energy are added to each beaker and the temperature change, ΔT, recorded. The results are shown in the table.

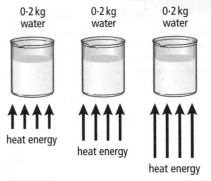

Heat energy added (J)	Temperature change ΔT (°C)
37 500	9
75 000	18
102 500	27

The results show that when equal masses of the same material are given different amounts of heat energy, the temperature change, ΔT, is different. Temperature change depends on the energy supplied; the greater the heat energy supplied, the larger the temperature change.

Experiment 3 - adding equal amounts of heat energy to different masses of the same material

The same amount of heat energy is added to different masses of aluminium, and the temperature change, ΔT, is recorded. The results are shown in the table.

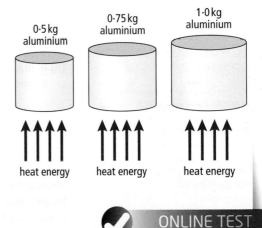

Mass of aluminium (kg)	Temperature change ΔT (°C)
0·5	48
0·75	36
1·0	24

The results show that when different masses of the same material are given equal amounts of heat energy, the temperature change, ΔT, is different. Temperature change depends on the mass of the material. The smaller mass has a greater temperature change.

 THINGS TO DO AND THINK ABOUT

Investigation

1. When two separate masses of water at different starting temperatures are mixed, the *final* temperature of the mixture lies between the two starting temperatures. How would you calculate the final temperature of the mixture?

2. Think about what happens to the heat energy of each liquid after they have mixed. Which one loses heat energy and which one gains heat energy?

3. What can you say about the heat energy lost by one mass and gained by the other? Could you use this information to write an equation which could be used to calculate the final temperature?

4. *Safely* prepare some masses of water at different temperatures.

5. Calculate the final temperature of the mixture, then *carefully* do the mixing to see if the final measured temperature agrees with your calculation.

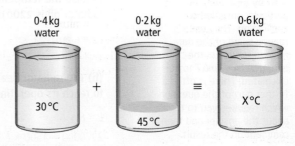

SPECIFIC HEAT CAPACITY 2

 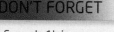
RELATIONSHIP FOR SPECIFIC HEAT CAPACITY

E_h, m, c, and ΔT are used together in a single relationship when heat energy, added or removed from a substance, causes a temperature change:

$$E_h = cm\Delta T$$ where: E_h is the heat energy added or removed (J)
c is the specific heat capacity of the substance ($J\,kg^{-1}\,°C^{-1}$).
m is the mass of the substance (kg).
ΔT is the temperature change of the substance (°C).

EXAMPLE 1

(a) How much heat energy is required to raise the temperature of 840 g of water on a cooker from 21°C to 84°C?

c for water = 4180J kg^{-1} $°C^{-1}$
(from the Data sheet)

First calculate ΔT = 84 −21 = 63°C
Convert 840g into 0·84kg

$E_h = cm\Delta T$
    = 4180 × 0·84 × 63
    = 221 206J

Pan of water on a cooker

(b) In practice, the actual amount of energy supplied by the cooker to cause this temperature rise is greater. Give one reason for this difference.

As the water is being heated, some heat will be lost to the surroundings, so more heat energy will be required from the cooker.

EXAMPLE 2

When 4·4 × 10⁴J of heat energy is added to a dinner plate in an oven, its temperature rises from 18°C to 87°C . The specific heat capacity of the dinner plate is 2700 J kg⁻¹ °C⁻¹. Calculate the mass of the plate.

ΔT = 87 − 18 = 69°C

$E_h = cm\Delta T$

4·4 × 10⁴ = 2700 × m × 69   so $m = \dfrac{4 \cdot 4 \times 10^4}{2700 \times 69} = 0 \cdot 24kg$

EXAMPLE 3

(a) An oil-filled radiator has an electric heater inside it to raise the temperature of 12·5 kg of oil to an operating temperature of 128°C. Calculate the energy required to raise the temperature of this oil from 20°C. The specific heat capacity of the radiator oil is 2200 J kg⁻¹°C⁻¹.

$E_h = cm\Delta T$ ΔT = 128 − 20 = 108 °C
    = 2200 × 12·5 × 108 = 2 970 000J

(b) The radiator heater is rated at 1500 W. Calculate the minimum time for the oil to reach its operating temperature.

$E = P \times t$

2 970 000 = 1500 × t **so** $t = \dfrac{2\,970\,000}{1500} = 1980s$

contd

(c) In practice, the actual time taken is greater than the minimum time calculated. Give one reason for this difference.

As the radiator is heated, some heat energy will be lost to the surroundings. More heat energy will be required to raise the temperature.

EXAMPLE 4

Disc brakes are used on mountain bikes to slow down quickly. They are usually made of iron which is quite heavy. When the brakes are applied, the kinetic energy of the bike and cyclist are converted into heat energy in the metal discs.

A manufacturer decided to reduce the **weight** of the bike by using aluminium disc brakes instead of iron. On the new model, the total mass of the aluminium disc brakes is 1·25 kg.

While testing this new bike, a cyclist travels down a steep hill using the brakes to slow down. During this braking, 676 500 J of kinetic energy is converted into heat energy in the disc brakes. Before braking, the temperature of the disc brakes is 25°C. Assume that all of the kinetic energy is converted into heat energy in the disc brakes.

(a) Calculate the final temperature of the brakes.

$E_h = cm\Delta T$

Specific heat capacity of aluminium = 902 J kg^{-1}°C^{-1} (obtained from the Data sheet)

$676\,500 = 902 \times 1·25 \times \Delta T$

$\Delta T = \dfrac{676\,500}{902 \times 1·25}$

$= 600\ °C$

Add the starting temperature to get the final temperature

$25 + 600 = 625°C$

Mountain bike showing detail of the disc brakes

(b) Explain why the final temperature is likely to be slightly less than that calculated above.

Some of the heat energy produced will be lost to the surroundings as the cyclist travels down the hill. This will reduce the final temperature.

(c) Use the Data sheet to comment on why the manufacturer decided that aluminium is unsuitable as a material for the disc brakes compared with iron.

The melting point of aluminium is 660°C (from the Data sheet). The final temperature of the aluminium is close to its melting point. The metal would become dangerously soft.

THINGS TO DO AND THINK ABOUT

Investigation

1. Some kettles have markers to tell you when there is enough water for one cup. What would you need to know to find out the difference in the electricity cost if the kettle is filled:

   • to the maximum level   • to one cupful level.

   (Hint: you need to find the *difference* in heat energy needed to heat one cupful and one full kettle to boiling from, say, 20°C.)

DON'T FORGET

The Data sheet in the exam may be required to obtain information not given in the question. Be familiar with each table in the sheet.

ONLINE TEST

For more questions on specific heat capacity at test yourself at www. brightredbooks.net/ N5Physics

ONLINE

Investigate more about specific heat capacity at www.brightredbooks.net/ N5Physics

DON'T FORGET

• Remember that heat energy can be added to or removed from a substance, and a temperature change can be an increase or decrease.
• Always select the value for c from the Data sheet, unless it is given in the question.
• When calculating the heat energy in specific heat capacity questions, it may be necessary to use one of a number of expressions for energy:
  $E = P \times t$ $E = (VI)t$
  $E = F \times d$ $E = \frac{1}{2}mv^2$
• The final parts of questions concerning heat energy often ask about improving an experiment, for example, how to reduce the amount of heat loss. Think carefully about the answer, which may be connected with insulating the container. (The answer can be as simple as putting a lid on a container!)

SPECIFIC LATENT HEAT

The key concepts to learn in this topic are:

- how substances change state from: solid ↔ liquid or liquid ↔ gas
- that the specific latent heat of **fusion**, l_f, of a substance is the heat energy required to change a mass of 1 kg of the substance from a solid at its melting point into liquid at the same temperature, or that the specific latent heat of **vaporisation**, l_v, of a substance is the heat energy required to change a mass of 1 kg of the substance from a liquid at its boiling point into a gas at the same temperature
- the use of an appropriate relationship to solve problems involving heat energy, mass and specific latent heat.

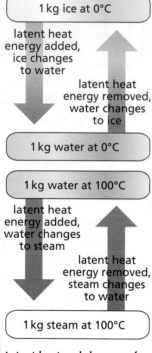

Latent heat and changes of state

CHANGE OF STATE

There are three states of matter – solid, liquid and gas.

The change of state from solid to liquid is called **fusion** or *melting*, and from liquid back to solid is called *solidifying* or *freezing*. The change of state from liquid to gas is called **vaporisation**, and gas to liquid is called **condensation**.

There is *no change in temperature* when a change of state takes place. So, when water at 100°C changes into steam at 100°C, the temperature remains constant. When heat energy is added to ice at 0°C, the ice eventually changes into the same mass of water, still at 0°C.

A solid substance at its melting point contains less heat energy than an equal mass of the same liquid substance at the melting point. The difference in energy is due to latent heat energy.

When a substance changes state, this happens at the *melting point* (in the case of fusion) or the *boiling point* (in the case of vaporisation) of the substance. The temperature remains constant.

Latent heat energy can be added or removed to cause the change of state. The energy required to change the state of a substance depends on the *mass* and *type* of substance and whether the change causes melting or vaporisation.

The energy needed to change the state of 1 kg of a substance from solid to liquid is called the specific latent heat of fusion $J\,kg^{-1}$ of the substance.

The energy needed for 1 kg of a substance to change state from liquid to gas is called the specific latent heat of vaporisation ($J\,kg^{-1}$) of the substance.

- l_f is the specific latent heat of fusion of a substance.
- l_v is the specific latent heat of vaporisation of a substance.

The relationship used to calculate the heat energy required to change the state of a substance of mass m is:

$E_h = ml_f$ for a substance at its melting point

$E_h = ml_v$ for a substance at its boiling point

There is no need for ΔT in these relationships as the temperature does not change.

EXAMPLE 1

Calculate the heat energy required to change 2·4 kg of solid iron into liquid iron.

The specific latent heat of fusion of iron = $2\cdot67 \times 10^5\,J\,kg^{-1}$ (from the Data sheet).

$E = ml_f = 2\cdot4 \times 2\cdot67 \times 10^5 = 640\,800\,J$

contd

EXAMPLE 2

A kettle with a power rating of 2·5 kW is filled with 1·2 kg of water and switched on by a student. When the kettle reaches boiling point, the automatic cut-off switch fails to operate and the kettle continues to heat the water for 4 minutes before it is switched off manually.

(a) Calculate the heat energy supplied by the kettle during the 4 minutes.

$E = Pt$ ($P = 2.5$ kW $= 2500$ W, $t = 4$ minutes $= 4 \times 60 = 240$ s)

$E = 2500 \times 240 = 6 \times 10^5$ J

(b) Calculate the mass of water remaining in the kettle after it is switched off.

The specific latent heat of vaporisation of water $= 22.6 \times 10^5$ J kg^{-1} (from the Data Sheet)

$E = ml_v$

$6 \times 10^5 = m \times 22.6 \times 10^5$ so $m = 0.27$ kg

So mass of water remaining in kettle $= 1.2 - 0.27 = 0.93$ kg

(c) Explain why this value is likely to be inaccurate.

While heating the water in the kettle, some heat energy will be lost to the surroundings instead of vaporising the water.

EXAMPLE 3

A solid of mass 125 g in a container is heated using a 50 W hotplate heater.

The graph shows how the temperature of the solid changes as it is heated from 25°C to 95°C.

(a) What is the melting point of the solid? Explain your answer.

The melting point is 50°C. The temperature of the solid remains constant at 50°C while it changes state to liquid.

(b) How long does it take for the solid to change state?

120 seconds.

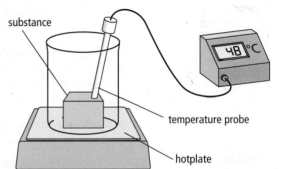

substance

temperature probe

hotplate

(c) How much heat energy was supplied to the solid while it changed state?

Power of heater $= P = 50$ W
Time taken to melt solid $= t = 120$ s

$E = Pt = 50 \times 120 = 6000$ J

(d) Calculate the specific latent heat of fusion of the solid.

Energy required to melt solid $= 6000$ J
Mass of solid $= 125$ g $= 0.125$ kg

$E = ml_f$
$6000 = 0.125 \times l_f$
$l_f = 4.8 \times 10^4$ J kg^{-1}

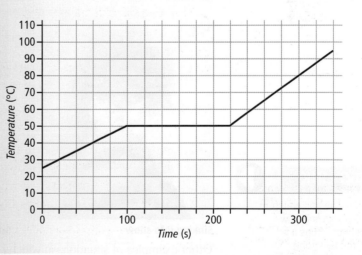

Time (s)

THINGS TO DO AND THINK ABOUT

1. Investigate how the energy transferred to ice when it melts is used to cool other objects down, e.g. ice packs applied to a sprained ankle.

2. Refrigerators keep food cool. Find out how the 'coolant liquid' used in fridges continually vaporises and condenses in order to transfer heat energy from food.

PRESSURE

The key concepts to learn in this topic are:

- that pressure is the force per unit area exerted on a surface
- the use of an appropriate relationship to solve problems involving pressure, force and area.

DEFINING PRESSURE

Pressure occurs when a force is applied to a surface. Whenever a force is applied to an object, pressure is exerted on the object. For example, the force can be caused by a hammer striking a nail, or by a molecule of a gas colliding with the walls of its container.

The relationship for pressure connects the force and the surface area of the object.

$$\text{pressure} = \frac{\text{force}}{\text{area}}$$

$$p = \frac{F}{A}$$

where p = pressure (Pa), F = force (N) and A = area (m^2)

The units for pressure are pascal (Pa) or newtons per square metre, (Nm^{-2}) and $1\,\text{Pa} = 1\,\text{Nm}^{-2}$.

The *larger* the force, the *greater* the pressure; the *larger* the area, the *smaller* the pressure. For example, a person standing on snow exerts a pressure on the snow through their feet because the feet are in contact with the ground. The area of the feet in contact with the snow is small, so the pressure on the snow is great and the person sinks into the snow.

If the person stands on skis, the area in contact with the snow is much greater, so the pressure on the snow is smaller and the person stays on the surface.

Sinking into snow

Staying on surface of snow

Other examples of situations in which pressure is important are:

- a sharp knife is used for cutting vegetables – the edge of the knife is very narrow, so a very small area is in contact with the vegetables; the pressure is very large and cutting is easier

- a camel has very large feet to spread the force of its weight over a large surface area – this prevents it sinking into soft sand in the desert

- farm tractors have very wide tyres to increase the area of each tyre that is in contact with the ground – this reduces the pressure of the heavy tractor on the soil.

contd

DON'T FORGET

Larger force means greater pressure; larger area means smaller pressure.

VIDEO LINK

Head online and watch the clip showing how polystyrene cups are affected by strong water pressure at www.brightredbooks.net/N5Physics

EXAMPLE 1

A 40 000 kg container rests on the trailer of a lorry.

(a) Calculate the force exerted by the container on the trailer.

The weight of the container causes a force on the trailer.

$F = mg = 40\,000 \times 9.8 = 392\,000\,\text{N}$

(b) The area of the container surface in contact with the trailer is 21 m². Calculate the pressure exerted on the trailer by the container.

$p = \dfrac{F}{A} = \dfrac{392\,000}{21} = 18\,667\,\text{Pa}$

EXAMPLE 2

A block of mass 45 kg has dimensions 3 m by 1 m by 40 cm. What is the greatest pressure that the block can exert on a flat horizontal surface?

The greatest pressure is exerted through the smallest face of the cube.

smallest area = $l \times b = 1 \times 0.4 = 0.4\,\text{m}^2$

$F = mg = 45 \times 9.8 = 441\,\text{N}$

$p = \dfrac{F}{A} = \dfrac{441}{0.4} = 1102.5\,\text{Pa}$

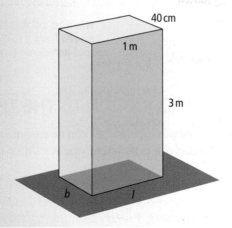

40 cm

1 m

3 m

b

l

DON'T FORGET

Area must always be given in square metres, so remember to convert centimetres or millimetres.

ONLINE TEST

For a test on pressure, visit www.brightredbooks.net/ N5Physics

THINGS TO DO AND THINK ABOUT

1. Using this knowledge about pressure, think of how to investigate:
   - the size of the pressure exerted by a drawing pin on a noticeboard
   - the pressure between a pencil and the paper it writes on.

   (Hint: think of how you would measure any of the required information needed to calculate the pressure. Make sure that you consider safety measures for any practical work.)

GAS LAWS: THREE EXPERIMENTS 1

This section follows on from the work on pressure. The key concepts to learn in this topic are:

- a description of how the kinetic model accounts for the pressure of a gas
- a knowledge of the relationship between kelvins and degrees celsius and the absolute zero of temperature
- how to explain the pressure-volume, pressure-temperature and volume-temperature laws qualitatively in terms of a kinetic model
- the use of appropriate relationships solve problems involving the volume, pressure and kelvin temperature of a fixed mass of gas.

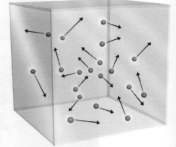

Gas particles in a sealed container

PROPERTIES OF GASES

When studying the properties of gases in containers, the temperature (T), pressure (p) and volume (V) can be easily measured using thermometers, pressure gauges and a gas syringe.

Measuring properties of gases

A gas in a sealed container has a *fixed* mass. So the number of gas particles (whether molecules or atoms) is fixed. There are three properties of the gas in the container:

- pressure, p
- temperature, T
- volume, V

When an inflated balloon is moved from a cold to a hotter spot its volume increases

A pressure cooker has a release valve to let hot steam out to reduce the pressure

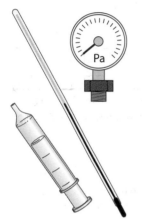

Measuring temperature, pressure and volume

VIDEO LINK

For another example of temperature affecting air pressure, watch the experiment with a hardboiled egg at www.brightredbooks.net/N5Physics

DON'T FORGET

Each experiment is always carried out using a fixed mass.

AN INTRODUCTION TO THE THREE GAS LAW EXPERIMENTS

Three separate experiments can be carried out to determine the relationship between p, T and V. In each experiment, one variable is kept constant to find how the remaining two variables are related:

- Experiment 1: V is constant; p and T are variable
- Experiment 2: p is constant; V and T are variable
- Experiment 3: T is constant; p and V are variable

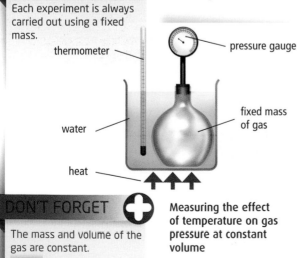

thermometer — pressure gauge

fixed mass of gas

water —

heat —

DON'T FORGET

The mass and volume of the gas are constant.

Measuring the effect of temperature on gas pressure at constant volume

EXPERIMENT 1: PRESSURE AND TEMPERATURE (THE PRESSURE LAW)

Here, we're investigating the relationship between pressure (p) and temperature (T) for a fixed mass of gas at *constant volume*.

In this experiment the temperature of gas inside a circular flask is changed and the changing gas pressure is recorded. It is assumed that the volume of the glass flask does not change when heated, and so the volume of the gas inside is also constant.

When a graph of pressure versus temperature is drawn, a straight line is obtained, but does not pass through the origin.

contd

Changing temperature and pressure at constant volume

The straight line on the graph has been projected until it reaches the temperature axis. Zero pressure is at –273°C. Zero pressure indicates the *true zero* of temperature. A lower temperature than this is not possible, which is why –273°C is known as **absolute zero**.

When the pressure versus temperature graph is redrawn with the temperature starting at –273°C, an alternative temperature scale called the *Kelvin scale* can be defined in which absolute zero is given as 0K.

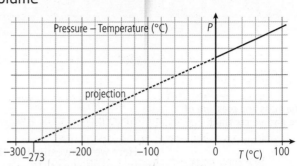

Pressure–temperature (°C) graph

Absolute zero of temperature

- The Kelvin scale uses the same divisions as the Celsius scale.
- So, one degree Celsius is the same size as one kelvin.
- The actual zero of the Kelvin scale is –273·15°C.

Converting between temperature scales

For most calculations the approximate value –273°C is used.

- To convert degrees Celsius into kelvin just add 273. For example, 25°C = 25 + 273 = 298K (the kelvin unit is simply K – no degrees!)
- To convert kelvin into degrees Celsius subtract 273. For example, 300K = 300 – 273 =27°C.

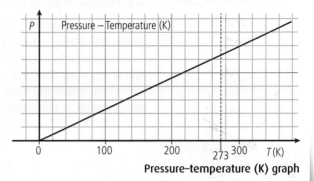

Pressure–temperature (K) graph

For Experiment 1, on the Kelvin scale, the straight line graph through the origin means that pressure is directly proportional to temperature in kelvin:

$$p \propto T \qquad \frac{p}{T} = k \text{ (where k = constant)} \qquad \frac{p_1}{T_1} = \frac{p_2}{T_2} \qquad \text{at constant volume.}$$
This is the *Pressure Law*.

Whenever this equation is used, the Celsius temperature of the gas must be converted into kelvin.

EXAMPLE:

A sample of gas in a sealed container is at a pressure of 200 kPa and at a temperature of 135°C. Calculate the new pressure if its temperature is reduced to 78°C and the volume of the container remains constant.

p_1 = 200 kPa, p_2 = ?, T_1 = 135°C, T_2 = 78°C

Convert T_1 and T_2 into kelvin for use in the equation:

T_1 = 135°C = 135 + 273 = 408K, T_2 = 78°C = 78 + 273 = 351K

$$\frac{p_1}{T_1} = \frac{p_2}{T_2} \Rightarrow \frac{200}{408} = \frac{p_2}{351}$$

$p_2 \times 408 = 200 \times 351$

p_2 = 172 kPa

Note that in this example, the pressure can remain in kPa in the calculation, but the temperature must always be converted from Celsius into kelvin.

THINGS TO DO AND THINK ABOUT

1. Use the Pressure Law to explain the following examples:

- Car tyre pressures need to be checked when winter weather arrives.
- When tackling industrial blazes, firefighters must be extremely careful – especially when there are gas cylinders present inside the factory.

GAS LAWS: THREE EXPERIMENTS 2

 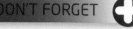
EXPERIMENT 2: VOLUME AND TEMPERATURE (CHARLES' LAW)

Here we're investigating the relationship between volume (V) and temperature (T) for a fixed mass of gas at constant *pressure*.

In this experiment the temperature of gas trapped in a long, narrow column of glass is altered and the changing volume of the gas is recorded. The water is heated slowly, so the gas inside the glass is the same temperature as the water.

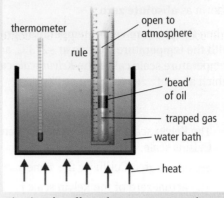

Investigating the effect of temperature on the volume of a fixed mass of gas at constant pressure

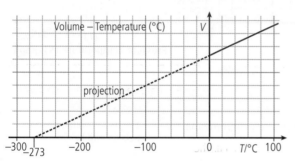

Volume–temperature (°C) graph

The bead inside the glass column moves so that the pressure of the trapped gas stays in equilibrium with atmospheric pressure (so pressure remains constant). When a graph of volume versus temperature is drawn, a straight line is obtained, but does not pass through the origin.

The straight line on the graph has been projected until it reaches the temperature axis. Zero volume appears at –273 °C. As we have seen, zero pressure indicates the true zero of temperature.

When the graph is redrawn with the temperature starting at –273°C, a new scale can be defined where absolute zero is 0K – the Kelvin scale.

On this Kelvin scale, the straight line graph through the origin means that volume is directly proportional to temperature in kelvin:

$$V \propto T \qquad \frac{V}{T} = k \text{ (where k = constant)} \qquad \frac{V_1}{T_1} = \frac{V_2}{T_2} \text{ at constant pressure.}$$

This is known as *Charles' law*.

Whenever this equation is used, Celsius temperatures must be converted into kelvin.

Volume–temperature (K) graph

EXAMPLE 1

A party balloon is inflated to a volume of 336 cm³ and sealed at a temperature of 29°C. During the night, its temperature falls to 3°C.

(a) Calculate the new volume of the balloon.

$V_1 = 336 \text{cm}^3$, $V_2 = ?$, $T_1 = 29°C$, $T_2 = 3°C$

Convert T_1 and T_2 into kelvin for use in the equation:

$T_1 = 29°C = 29 + 273 = 302K$, $T_2 = 3°C = 3 + 273 = 276K$

$\frac{V_1}{T_1} = \frac{V_2}{T_2} \qquad \frac{336}{302} = \frac{V_2}{276}$

$V_2 \times 302 = 336 \times 276 = 307 \cdot 1 \text{cm}^3$

Note that in this question, the volume can remain in cm³ in the calculation, but the temperature must be converted from Celsius into kelvin.

(b) State any assumptions that you have made.

The answer to part (a) assumes that no air leaked from the balloon and that the air pressure remained constant overnight while the balloon reduced in size.

 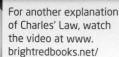

EXPERIMENT 3: VOLUME AND PRESSURE (BOYLE'S LAW)

Here we're investigating the relationship between volume (V) and pressure (p) for a fixed mass of gas at constant temperature. In this experiment the pressure of gas inside a syringe is changed by pressing the plunger and each new volume of the gas is recorded. The plunger is pressed slowly, so the gas inside the syringe stays at constant temperature.

When a graph of volume versus pressure is drawn, a curve is obtained, which shows that as the pressure increases, the volume decreases.

When a graph of 1/volume versus pressure is drawn, a straight line through the origin is obtained.

This means that the pressure is inversely proportional to the volume:

$$p \propto \frac{1}{V} \qquad pV = k \text{ (where k = constant)}$$

$$p_1 V_1 = p_2 V_2$$

at constant temperature.

This is known as *Boyle's law*.

pressure gauge

plunger

pressure sensor syringe

Volume–pressure graph

$\frac{1}{volume}$**–pressure graph**

EXAMPLE 2

Gas contained in a syringe has a volume of 55 cm³ and is at a pressure of $2\cdot34 \times 10^4$ Pa. The syringe is compressed until the new volume is 27 cm³. Assume that the temperature remains constant.

(a) Calculate the new pressure of the gas in the syringe.

$V_1 = 55\text{cm}^3$, $V_2 = 27\text{cm}^3$, $p_1 = 2\cdot34 \times 10^4$ Pa, $p_2 = ?$

$p_1 V_1 = p_2 V_2$

$2\cdot34 \times 10^4 \times 55 = p_2 \times 27$

$p_2 = \dfrac{2\cdot34 \times 10^4 \times 55}{27} = 4\cdot77 \times 10^4$ Pa

(b) In practice, as it is compressed, the temperature of the gas rises. Explain what effect this may have on the final pressure of the gas.

If the gas temperature rises, then the kinetic energy and **average velocity** of the gas particles will increase. This will cause more collisions and greater force of collisions, causing the pressure to increase.

THINGS TO DO AND THINK ABOUT

1. Consider which individual gas equation explains each of these phenomena:
   - A football, inflated indoors and then taken outside on a cold day, shrinks slightly.
   - Deep sea divers breathe a mixture of oxygen and helium when submerged, and sometimes return to the surface in stages.
   - Deep sea fish die when they are brought to the surface, even if kept in water tanks.
   - People's ears sometimes 'pop' in an aircraft at take-off and landing.
   - A hot air balloon rises when the trapped air inside the balloon is heated.

2. Research the uses of 'superconductors' – when wires conduct at extremely low temperatures.

GAS LAWS: USING THE GENERAL GAS EQUATION

THE GENERAL GAS EQUATION

The three gas laws can be combined into one *general gas equation*, in which p, V and T are all variable.

1: $\dfrac{p_1}{T_1} = \dfrac{p_2}{T_2}$ 2: $\dfrac{V_1}{T_1} = \dfrac{V_2}{T_2}$ 3: $p_1 V_1 = p_2 V_2$

The three equations above combine to make the general gas equation:

$$\frac{pV}{T} = k \text{ (where k = constant)} \qquad \text{or} \qquad \frac{p_1 V_1}{T_1} = \frac{p_2 V_2}{T_2}$$

EXAMPLE:

A weather balloon is inflated to $2\cdot83\,m^3$ at the Earth's surface at a pressure of $1\cdot01 \times 10^5\,Pa$. The temperature of the air inside the balloon is 28°C. When the balloon is released into the atmosphere it rises to an altitude of 47 km where the air pressure is 111 Pa and the volume of the balloon increases to $269\,m^3$.

Calculate the air temperature at this altitude.

$V_1 = 2\cdot83m^3$, $V_2 = 269m^3$, $T_1 = 28°C$, $T_2 = ?$, $p_1 = 1\cdot01 \times 10^5$ Pa, $p_2 = 111Pa$

Convert T_1 into kelvin for use in the equation: $T_1 = 28°C = 28 + 273 = 301K$

$$\frac{p_1 V_1}{T_1} = \frac{p_2 V_2}{T_2}$$

$$\frac{1\cdot01 \times 10^5 \times 2\cdot83}{301} = \frac{111 \times 269}{T_2} \quad \text{so} \quad T_2 = \frac{111 \times 269 \times 301}{1\cdot01 \times 10^5 \times 2\cdot83} = 31\cdot4 \text{ K}$$

DON'T FORGET

Remember to convert temperatures into kelvin!

DON'T FORGET

The kinetic theory of gases is when the behaviour of the particles in a gas is used to explain the relationship between the pressure, volume and temperature of the gas.

VIDEO LINK

Watch the simulation of gas particles at www.brightredbooks.net/N5Physics

KINETIC MODEL OF A GAS

A container filled with any gas contains millions of tiny particles, continually and freely moving in random directions at high speeds. When these moving gas particles collide with each other, or with the walls of their container, no energy is lost.

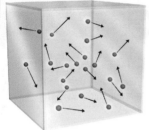

Gas particles in a sealed container

GAS PRESSURE

The pressure exerted by a gas is caused by the moving particles that collide with the walls of the gas container. Each collision causes the wall to receive a tiny force. The size of the pressure depends on the *number of collisions* and the *average force per collision* exerted on the area of the walls.

For example, if you cover the end of a bicycle pump with your thumb and press the plunger, it becomes very hard to keep your thumb in position because the gas pressure inside the pump increases. As the particles move, they collide with other particles and also with the inside walls of the pump. The pressure that you feel is due to the average force produced by millions of particle collisions with your thumb!

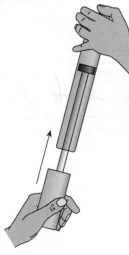

Increasing the pressure inside a bicycle pump

GAS VOLUME

The volume of a gas is the amount of space the particles have to move around. If the walls of the container are brought closer, there will be less time between collisions with the wall. In the bicycle pump example, the volume is reduced when the plunger is pressed – hence more collisions per second with your thumb, leading to greater force and pressure!

GAS TEMPERATURE AND MEAN KINETIC ENERGY

Gas particles are continually moving at different velocities inside the container. When heat energy is added to the gas, this increases both the **velocity** and the kinetic energy of the particles. The gas temperature T is proportional to the mean kinetic energy of these particles (but not the velocity).

AIR PRESSURE

The air in the atmosphere extends about 120 km above us. The pressure exerted by gas particles in the air is known as atmospheric pressure. Millions of gas particles are continually colliding with the Earth's surface (and us!), each one exerting a tiny force. The result of all of these collisons is to produce atmospheric (or air) pressure.

The value for normal atmospheric pressure is 101 000 Pa ($1·01 × 10^5$ Pa) . This is equivalent to a force of 100 000 N acting on one square metre of surface.

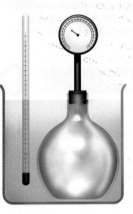

Air particles colliding with a surface

THE GAS LAWS AND THE KINETIC MODEL

Each of the gas laws can be explained in terms of the behaviour of gas particles.

1 The pressure-temperature law (the pressure law, constant volume, p ∝T)

If the gas temperature increases, the particles have more kinetic energy and they move faster. The particles hit the walls with greater average force. Also, because the volume is constant, they hit the container walls more often. These two effects cause an increase in pressure.

2 The volume-temperature law (Charles' law, constant pressure, V ∝ T)

If the temperature increases, the particles have more kinetic energy and they move faster. The particles hit the container walls with more force which causes the gas pressure to increase. This increase in pressure causes the gas volume to increase, which results in fewer collisions each second. When the inside pressure is the same as the outside pressure the volume stops increasing.

Changing temperature and pressure of a constant volume

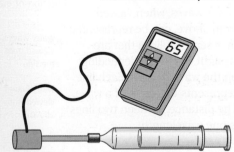

Changing temperature and volume at constant pressure

The pressure-volume law (Boyle's Law, constant temperature)

As the temperature is constant, the average kinetic energy and the velocity are constant. This means that the particles hit the walls of the container with the same average force. When the gas volume is increased, the particles have to travel further between collisions with the container walls. There are fewer particle collisions per second. This causes the pressure to fall.

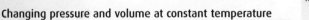

Changing pressure and volume at constant temperature

DON'T FORGET

The kinetic model uses the motion of the particles to explain the gas laws.

ONLINE TEST

Visit www.brightredbooks. net/N5Physics to test your knowledge of the gas laws.

⚠ THINGS TO DO AND THINK ABOUT

1. Atmospheric weather balloons rise to enormous altitudes, to capture data required for weather forecasting. The air pressure and temperature reduce at such altitudes. Carry out research to find out the balloon dimensions, what data they collect and what eventually happens to them.

WAVES AND RADIATION

WAVE PARAMETERS AND BEHAVIOURS 1

The key concepts to learn in this topic are:

- energy can be transferred as waves
- how to determine the frequency, period, wavelength, amplitude and wave speed for longitudinal and transverse waves
- the use of appropriate relationships to solve

problems involving wave speed, frequency, period, wavelength, distance, number of waves and time

- to understand the diffraction of waves, including the practical limitations of demonstrating diffraction; and a comparison of long wave and short wave diffraction.

ONLINE

For more details on the key concepts for this topic, go to www.brightredbooks.net/N5Physics

VIDEO LINK

Check out the clip on particle motion at www.brightredbooks.net/N5Physics

THE TRANSFER OF ENERGY IN WAVES

Waves are created by **vibration**. Waves transfer energy from one place to another. For example, when waves reach the seashore, the water particles are vibrating. (This means that the water particles have kinetic energy (E_k) when they are moving and potential energy (E_p) when they are displaced from their resting position.)

Energy is transferred across the sea from the place where the waves were created (usually by winds and tides).

Waves crashing ashore can transfer so much energy that they cause damage

a = amplitude λ = wavelength

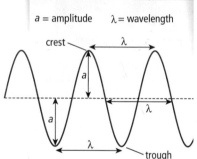

The diagram shows how the various parts of a wave are usually represented

VIDEO LINK

A slinky spring can show how the particles move in each type of wave: www.brightredbooks.net/N5Physics

DON'T FORGET

Energy moves through a medium; the particles just vibrate.

DON'T FORGET

You need to be able to work out amplitude and wavelength from the type of wave diagram in Example 1.

TYPES OF WAVES

There are two types of waves:

Sound energy is transferred by **longitudinal waves**. Light energy is transferred by **transverse waves.** Water and sound waves require particles to vibrate in order for energy to be transferred.

Water waves, when viewed from above, can be represented by a series of lines that are straight or curved depending on the wave pattern. Each line represents the **crest** of a wave. The distance between two lines is one wavelength.

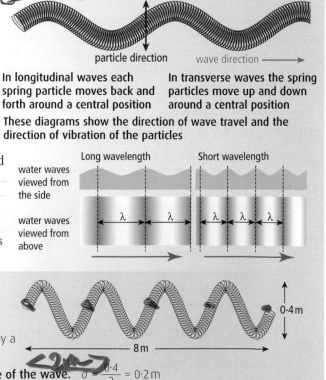

In longitudinal waves each spring particle moves back and forth around a central position

In transverse waves the spring particles move up and down around a central position

These diagrams show the direction of wave travel and the direction of vibration of the particles

EXAMPLE 1

A slinky is used to show some wave properties. A simplified diagram of a wave produced by a slinky is shown here.

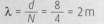

(a) Determine the amplitude of the wave. $a = \frac{0.4}{2} = 0.2\,\text{m}$

(b) Calculate the wavelength of the wave.

There are four complete waves in 8 m. So, d = length all four waves = 8 m.

N = number of complete waves = 4 waves

$\lambda = \frac{d}{N} = \frac{8}{4} = 2\,\text{m}$

contd

Amplitude is half peak to peak to trough.

EXAMPLE 2

A ripple tank is a device that is used to demonstrate the properties of water waves. A ripple tank was used to show water waves travelling from deep to shallow water. The diagram represents the water waves before and after they reach the shallow water.

Calculate the wavelength of the water waves: (a) in deep water   (b) in shallow water.

(a) One wave between each crest → 4 waves in 30 cm   Deep: $\lambda = \dfrac{d}{N} = \dfrac{30}{4} = 7.5$ cm

(b) One wave between each crest → 4 waves in 20 cm   Shallow: $\lambda = \dfrac{d}{N} = \dfrac{20}{4} = 5.0$ cm

deep water   shallow water

30 cm   20 cm

Water waves

ENERGY OF A WAVE

The energy transferred by waves depends on their amplitude.

The greater the wave amplitude, the greater the energy transferred

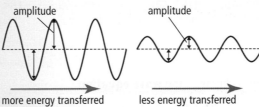

amplitude

amplitude

more energy transferred

less energy transferred

DON'T FORGET

Greater wave amplitude = greater energy transferred.

WAVE DEFINITIONS

Wave frequency, f, is calculated by counting the number of waves produced in a certain time, then calculating the number produced each second.

The period, T, and frequency, f, of waves are connected by the relationship: $f = \dfrac{1}{T}$

Using this equation, frequency can be calculated if the period of the wave is known.

Quantity	Symbol	Definition	Unit
Wavelength	λ (lambda)	The shortest distance before the wave pattern repeats	metre, m
Frequency	f	Number of waves that pass a point in one second	hertz, Hz
Wave speed	v	The distance travelled in unit time	metres per second, ms^{-1}
Amplitude	a	Distance from the rest position to the top of a **crest** or the bottom of a **trough**	metres, m
Period	T	The time for one wave to be produced	second, s

EXAMPLE 3

A tuning fork produces 41 880 vibrations in 2 minutes. Calculate the frequency of the note produced.

frequency = number of vibrations each second: $f = \dfrac{\text{number of vibrations}}{\text{time taken in seconds}} = \dfrac{41880}{2 \times 60} = 349$ Hz

A tuning fork

EXAMPLE 4

The **oscilloscope** wave pattern represents an electrical signal.

Determine: (a) the amplitude of the signal

amplitude, a = distance from centre to top of signal
        = 30 mV

(b) the frequency of the signal.

period, T, of wave from graph = 6 μs

$f = \dfrac{1}{T} = \dfrac{1}{6 \times 10^{-6}} = 1.7 \times 10^5$ Hz

Voltage (mV)

Time (μs)

DON'T FORGET

When using frequency and time, always covert into hertz and seconds.

ONLINE TEST

How well have you learned about the energy of waves and wave parameters? Go online and test yourself at www.brightredbooks.net/N5Physics

THINGS TO DO AND THINK ABOUT

1. Wave energy can be harnessed by offshore wave generators. Research the requirements for installing these devices:
   - the minimum depth of water
   - how much energy can be generated
   - how they can be connected to the National Grid
   - the best locations around Scotland for placing the generators.

2. State the advantages and disadvantages of installing these devices.

WAVE PARAMETERS AND BEHAVIOURS 2

THE WAVE EQUATION

Wavespeed, v, is the distance travelled by a wave in one second. To calculate **wavespeed** you can use one of two methods.

Method 1

The wavespeed, v, can be calculated by multiplying the wavelength, λ, by the frequency, f.

$$v = f\lambda$$

This is know as the **wave equation**.

Method 2

The wavespeed, v, can also be calculated by dividing the distance travelled by the wave, d, by the time, t.

$$v = \frac{d}{t}$$

(handwritten note) △ Method y preferred

EXAMPLE 1

A person aboard a boat anchored at sea counts 24 waves passing the boat in 2 minutes. The time for a wave crest to travel from the boat to a buoy is 42 s. The buoy is 140 m from the boat.

Determine:
(a) the speed of the waves

The waves travel 140 m in 42 seconds.

$$v = \frac{d}{t} = \frac{140}{42} = 3.3 \text{ m s}^{-1}$$

(b) the frequency of the waves

24 waves pass the buoy in 120 seconds.

$$f = \frac{\text{number of waves}}{\text{time taken}} = \frac{24}{120} = 0.2 \text{ Hz}$$

(c) the wavelength of the waves.

$$\lambda = \frac{v}{f} = \frac{3.3}{0.2} = 16.5 \text{ m}$$

EXAMPLE 2

The 'sodium doublet' is the name given to two spectral lines of the element sodium which are used by optical scientists as 'benchmarks' when checking instruments that measure wavelength. The doublet consists of two yellow lines close together in the **visible spectrum**.

The wavelengths of the lines are 589·0 nm and 589·6 nm. Calculate the difference in frequencies of these lines.

Both waves travel at speed of light in a vacuum = 3×10^8 m s^{-1}

$$f_1 = \frac{v}{\lambda} = \frac{3 \times 10^8}{589 \times 10^{-9}} = 5.093 \times 10^{14} \text{ Hz}$$

$$f_2 = \frac{v}{\lambda} = \frac{3 \times 10^8}{589.6 \times 10^{-9}} = 5.088 \times 10^{14} \text{ Hz}$$

$$\Delta f = f_1 - f_2 = 5.093 \times 10^{14} - 5.088 \times 10^{14} = 5.0 \times 10^{11} \text{ Hz}$$

contd

DIFFRACTION

All waves display several common behaviours:

- They all transfer energy.
- They all exhibit the properties of reflection, refraction, diffraction and interference.

Diffraction is the property of waves which occurs when they *bend* around obstacles. Diffraction can be demonstrated using water waves.

Diffraction around obstacles

Waves diffract (bend) into the gaps behind obstacles when they pass by. Note that when waves are diffracted, their *wavelength* does not change. But, the longer the wavelength, the greater the diffraction.

A practical example of this concerns television and radio signal reception.

Television and **radio signals** travel as **electromagnetic waves** and both travel at the speed of light. **Television waves** have a much greater frequency than **radio waves**, and so have a much shorter wavelength.

A house situated behind a hill from the **transmitter** (as shown in the diagram) relies on diffraction of the signals around the hilltop to reach the aerial. Radio waves have much longer wavelengths than TV waves, and so diffract more. So the house receives radio signals, but not TV signals.

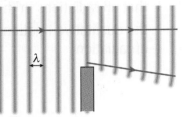
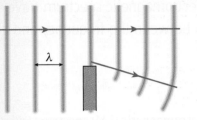

Low-frequency long wavelengths: most diffraction.

High-frequency short wavelengths: least diffraction.

Diffraction around obstacles

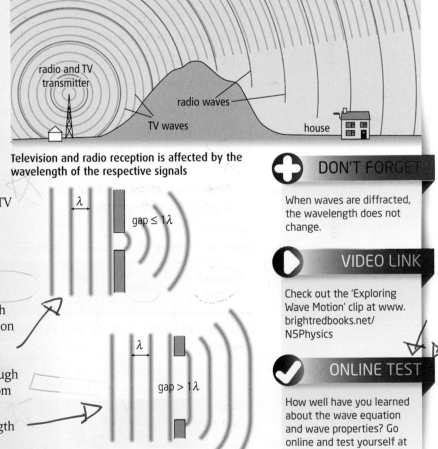

Television and radio reception is affected by the wavelength of the respective signals

Diffraction through gaps

Diffraction also occurs when waves pass through gaps.

When waves pass through a gap, the width of the gap determines how much diffraction occurs:

- If the gap is less than or equal to the wavelength of the waves passing through (gap ⩽ 1 λ), circular waves emerge from the gap.
- If the gap is greater than the wavelength (gap > λ), straight waves emerge, diffracted at their edges.

gap ≤ 1λ

gap > 1λ

Diffraction through gaps

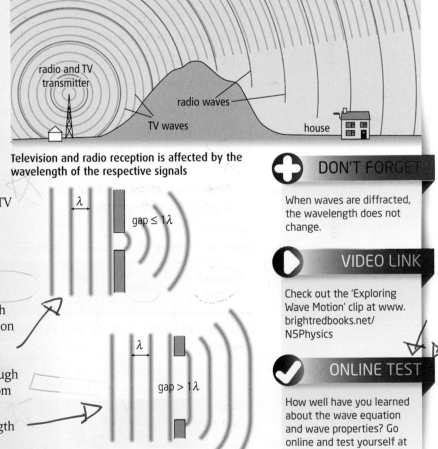

DON'T FORGET

When waves are diffracted, the wavelength does not change.

VIDEO LINK

Check out the 'Exploring Wave Motion' clip at www.brightredbooks.net/N5Physics

ONLINE TEST

How well have you learned about the wave equation and wave properties? Go online and test yourself at www.brightredbooks.net/N5Physics

THINGS TO DO AND THINK ABOUT

1. Investigate some phenomena caused by diffraction. For example:

(a) Why can we hear sounds from behind obstacles, but cannot see light from behind obstacles?

(b) Why does thunder sound like a low rumble when a storm is distant, but sound like a sharp crack when the storm is close by?

ELECTROMAGNETIC SPECTRUM 1

The key concepts to learn in this topic are:

- a knowledge of the relative frequency and wavelength of bands of the electromagnetic spectrum with reference to typical sources, detectors and applications
- that all radiations in the electromagnetic spectrum travel at the speed of light
- the qualitative relationship between the frequency and energy associated with a form of radiation

AN OVERVIEW

The **electromagnetic (EM) spectrum** is the name given to a family of waves. These waves do *not* require any moving particles to transfer their energy. Electromagnetic waves consist of vibrating electric and magnetic fields. The energy transferred by these waves is referred to as electromagnetic *radiation*.

The different parts of the EM spectrum have the following properties in common:

- they are all able to travel through a vacuum
- they all transfer energy
- they all travel at the speed of light in a vacuum ($3 \times 10^8 \, \text{m s}^{-1}$)
- they all exhibit wave properties of reflection, refraction, diffraction and interference and obey the wave equation ($v = f\lambda$).

Although they all travel at the same speed, different parts of the spectrum have different *wavelengths* and *frequencies*.

This diagram of the EM spectrum displays the names, relative wavelengths and frequencies of its different parts.

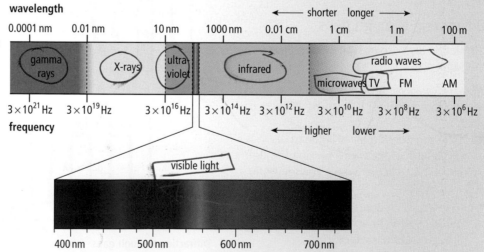

The electromagnetic spectrum

The order of the seven different parts of the spectrum is determined by their wave frequency.

The frequency and wavelength are inversely proportional. In the EM spectrum, as the wave frequency increases, the wavelength decreases.

contd

EXAMPLE:

UVB ultraviolet radiation can cause tanning, sunburn and skin cancer. UVB wavelengths range from 280–320 nm. Calculate the frequency range of these waves.

All EM spectrum waves travel at 3×10^8 m s⁻¹.

$\lambda_1 = 280 \times 10^{-9}$ m

$f_1 = \dfrac{v}{\lambda}$

$= \dfrac{3 \times 10^8}{280 \times 10^{-9}}$

$= 1 \cdot 07 \times 10^{15}$ Hz

$\lambda_2 = 320 \times 10^{-9}$ m

$f_2 = \dfrac{v}{\lambda}$

$= \dfrac{3 \times 10^8}{320 \times 10^{-9}}$

$= 9 \cdot 38 \times 10^{14}$ Hz

So the frequency range is $9 \cdot 38 \times 10^{14}$ Hz to $1 \cdot 07 \times 10^{15}$ Hz.

The energy which the electromagnetic waves transfer is proportional to the frequency of their radiation.

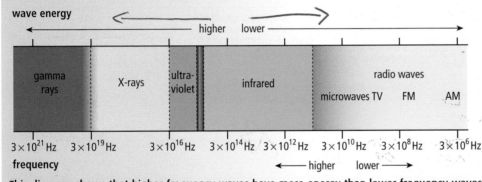

This diagram shows that higher frequency waves have more energy than lower frequency waves

Gamma radiation has the highest frequency range, which means that these are the waves with the highest energy in the EM spectrum.

 THINGS TO DO AND THINK ABOUT

The Sun and stars all give out radiation from the EM spectrum, although the Earth's atmosphere filters out some parts of the spectrum before they reach the surface.

1. Find out which parts of the atmosphere absorb which parts of the spectrum.

2. How is research carried out on the radiations which do not reach the surface of the Earth?

DON'T FORGET

The greater the frequency, the greater the energy of the waves in the electromagnetic spectrum.

ONLINE TEST

Take the 'Electromagnetic spectrum' test online at www.brightredbooks.net/N5Physics

ONLINE

For more information, follow the electromagnetic spectrum link at www.brightredbooks.net/N5Physics

ELECTROMAGNETIC SPECTRUM 2

COMMON SOURCES AND APPLICATIONS OF ELECTROMAGNETIC RADIATION

The different radiations of the electromagnetic spectrum have many applications. The Sun and stars are sources of all radiations present in the electromagnetic spectrum. However, the most common applications involve sources which are produced on Earth.

	Typical sources	Detector	Applications and uses	Additional facts
Gamma rays	· Radioactive substances · Nuclear reactors	· **Geiger–Muller tube** and **counter**	· Medical diagnosis using **radioisotopes** as **gamma ray** tracers · Sterilisation of medical instruments · Scanning shipping containers at ports	· Highest energy of EM spectrum · Cannot penetrate Earth's atmosphere from outer space · Causes **ionisation**, which can affect living tissue
X-rays	· **X-rays** are caused when very fast moving electrons collide with a metal target · X-ray machines	· X-rays darken photographic film · X-ray image intensifiers · Geiger–Muller tube and counter	· Medical imaging, giving 3D images of the internal body structure, used especially in the diagnosis of broken bones · Analysis of atomic structures using X-ray crystallography · Airport security scanners	· High energy waves · Cannot penetrate Earth's atmosphere from outer space · Causes ionisation, which can affect living tissue
Ultraviolet radiation	· The Sun is an important source of **UV radiation** · UV lamps, including mercury vapour lamps	· UV radiation causes some materials to 'fluoresce' i.e. glow when exposed to UV · A UV photodiode is an electronic device which detects UV	· UV radiation causes a chemical reaction in the skin that produces the important nutrient vitamin D · UV radiation is used in the treatment of certain skin conditions · Disinfection of hospital equipment · Used by dentists to 'cure' or harden composite material used for fillings	· Most UV radiation from the Sun is absorbed in the upper atmosphere by the ozone layer · The UV radiation range is sometimes separated into three bands: UVA, UVB and UVC · UVC is the highest frequency UV (hence the highest energy) and, fortunately, is filtered out by the ozone layer · UVA and UVB radiation cause sunburn and tanning, and overexposure can cause skin cancer · Causes ionisation, which can affect living tissue
Visible light	· The Sun is a primary source of visible light · Light bulbs, lasers	· Photodiodes · Phototransistors · Light dependent resistors detect light energy	· Light from lasers is widely used in communication through optical fibres · Supermarket checkout readers use laser light to scan barcodes for information · Laser light is used in medical treatment and surgery	· The eye responds to visible light, which occupies the smallest range of wavelengths in the EM spectrum · Red light has the longest and blue light has the shortest wavelength in the spectrum

contd

	Typical sources	Detector	Applications and uses	Additional facts
Infrared rays	· **Infrared radiation** is received from the Sun · Infrared heaters	· (Black bulb) thermometer · Thermopile	· Used as heating source · Humans emit infrared radiation – 'night/thermal image' IR cameras are used to detect infrared radiation in darkness, and to locate trapped disaster survivors · Used in medical diagnosis and treatment · Passive infrared detectors (PID) are used in intruder alarms	· Infrared rays (heat rays) are responsible for heat transfer by radiation · Over half of the radiation received on Earth from the Sun is infrared radiation · Most of the emitted energy from Earth through the atmosphere back into space is in the form of infrared radiation · The surface temperature of the Earth is regulated by the re-radiating of this radiation – this maintains the average temperature of the planet
Microwaves	· Microwave ovens produce waves (called microwaves) with a wavelength of approximately 3 cm	· Radar detector dishes	· Used extensively for communication, for example in **satellite** phones and television outside broadcasts	
Radio waves	· Radio waves are made by various transmitters	· TV aerials · Radar detector dishes	· Used extensively for communication · Transmitters connected to amplifiers produce radio waves	· The wide range of radio frequencies is used for many different types of communication · Radio wave transmitters can range in size from small enough to fit inside a mobile phone, to around 550 m for a TV **transmitter**

EXAMPLE:

The electromagnetic spectrum is shown here in order with some radiations missing.

gamma	A	ultraviolet	B	infrared	microwaves	radio waves

(a) Name radiations A and B.

A = X-rays, B = visible light.

(b) Which radiation has the lowest energy?

Radio waves have the lowest energy.

(c) Which radiation has the highest frequency?

Gamma radiation has the highest frequency.

THINGS TO DO AND THINK ABOUT

1. Find out more about sources, detectors and uses of the EM spectrum.

2. Try to investigate in more detail how the detectors actually work.

3. Are there any safety considerations which affect the use of electromagnetic radiation? For example, what are the problems, if any, associated with the use of microwave ovens?

VIDEO LINK

For further information on this topic, watch 'The Electromagnetic Spectrum' at www.brightredbooks.net/N5Physics

DON'T FORGET

Sources, applications and detectors for different parts of the electromagnetic spectrum can be asked about in the exam.

ONLINE TEST

Take the 'Electromagnetic spectrum' test online at www.brightredbooks.net/N5Physics

LIGHT

The key concepts to learn in this topic are:

- to identify the normal, angle of incidence and angle of refraction, in ray diagrams showing refraction
- to describe refraction in terms of change of wavelength and change of direction (where the angle of incidence is greater than 0°).

REFRACTION

Refraction is the change in speed of light when it travels from one material to another.

When light travels from a *less dense to a more dense* material (such as from air into glass), its *wavelength decreases*, it *slows down* and changes direction (or refracts) *towards the normal*. When light travels from a *more dense to a less dense* material (from glass into air), its *wavelength increases*, it *speeds up* and changes direction *away from the normal*.

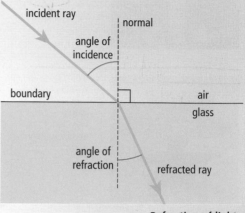

Refraction of light

The amount of refraction depends on the type of materials used.

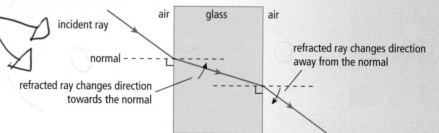

This diagram illustrates the changes in direction of refracted light

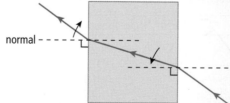

This diagram illustrates that the ray of light would have exactly the same path if it were directed into the glass from the reverse direction.

When the angle of incidence is 0°, the light ray passes straight through

The refraction of light can cause some unusual effects. For example, when observing a straight stick that is partly submerged in water, it appears bent.

The explanation involves the refraction of light. When light from the submerged part of the stick reaches the surface, it is refracted away from the normal. When this light enters our eyes, the image of the stick appears to be closer to the surface than it should be.

An unusual effect of refraction

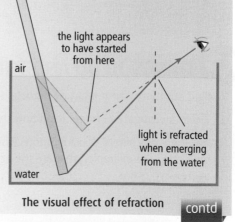

The visual effect of refraction

contd

Lenses

Convex and **concave** lenses are used to refract light for particular applications. Lenses are used in optical instruments, including spectacles, cameras, microscopes and telescopes.

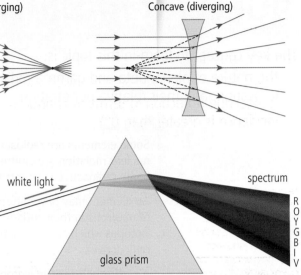

Convex (converging)

Concave (diverging)

Prisms

A **prism** is a three-dimensional triangular piece of glass (or transparent plastic) which is used to refract light.

Different colours of light are refracted by different amounts. A ray of white light directed into a prism will be refracted to show the different colours of the visible spectrum.

Prisms can be used to analyse a light source to determine the colours of light present in the incident ray.

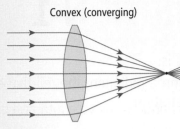

white light

spectrum

R O Y G B I V

glass prism

Light of different colours is refracted by different amounts

REFRACTION EXAMPLES

EXAMPLE 1

Light passes from air into glass. This process is called refraction.

(a) Explain what is meant by refraction.

Refraction is the change of speed and wavelength of waves when they travel from one material into another.

(b) Draw a labelled diagram showing the path of a ray of light being refracted as it passes into a glass block. Label the incident ray, the refracted ray, the normal, the angle of incidence and the angle of refraction.

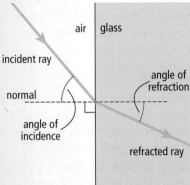

air | glass

incident ray

normal

angle of incidence

angle of refraction

refracted ray

EXAMPLE 2

A ray of green light is incident on a glass block as shown.

Calculate the angle of incidence and angle of refraction.

angle of incidence = 90° – 38° = 52°

angle of refraction = 90° – 59° = 31°

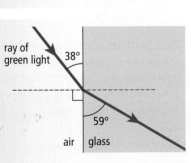

ray of green light

38°

59°

air | glass

THINGS TO DO AND THINK ABOUT

Refraction of light in glass has many uses in optical instruments, some of which have had a great impact on society.

1. Research the effects on light rays when they pass through convex and concave lenses.

2. Find out how refraction in the glass lenses used in spectacles allows wearers who are short or long sighted to be able to see clearly.

NUCLEAR RADIATION 1

The key concept to learn in this topic is:

- the nature of alpha, beta and gamma radiation, the relative effect of their ionisation, and their relative penetration.

Some elements are radioactive. This means that they emit radiation. Three types of nuclear radiation are emitted by radioactive elements: alpha, beta and gamma radiation. Some radioactive elements occur naturally and some are created artificially.

An element may have different **isotopes**. Isotopes of an element have different numbers of neutrons in their **nucleus**, but are still the same element. Some elements have isotopes which are radioactive while other isotopes of the element are stable (that is *not* radioactive).

A **radionuclide** is an isotope of an element which is radioactive.

TYPES OF NUCLEAR RADIATION

The three types of nuclear radiation are shown in the diagrams below.

The atoms of radioactive substances emit radiation. Nuclear radiation is emitted from the nucleus at the centre of the atom. All types of radiation can be harmful, but may also be very useful when carefully employed; so it is important to know exactly how each type of radiation behaves.

Alpha facts

- Alpha particles are large positive nuclei (equivalent to the nuclei of helium atoms).
- They are emitted from radioactive atoms when they decay (give out radiation).
- Alpha particles are slow moving (at approximately 5% of the speed of light).
- They cause greatest ionisation (or greatest ionisation density) because of their large size.

Alpha (α) radiation

alpha particle

2 neutrons   2 protons

Beta facts

- Beta particles are emitted when neutrons in the nuclei of radioactive atoms are converted into electrons (beta particles) and protons.
- A beta particle is a very fast moving electron (travelling at approximately 90% of the speed of light).
- They cause weak ionisation.

Beta (β) radiation

beta particle = 1 electron

Gamma facts

- Gamma rays are emitted when a radioactive atom decays, sometimes when alpha or beta particles are also emitted.
- Gamma rays are waves of energy and are part of the electromagnetic spectrum.
- They travel at the speed of light.
- Gamma rays are electromagnetic waves and cause very weak ionisation.

Gamma (γ) radiation

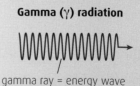

gamma ray = energy wave

Types of radiation

ABSORPTION OF RADIATION

It is vital to know how far radiation can travel (or penetrate) before it is absorbed and is no longer dangerous. This knowledge allows us to select materials for shielding humans from the radiation.

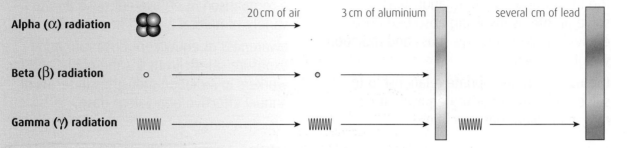

Different types of radiation penetrate materials to different degrees

Alpha radiation can only travel a few centimetres in air before being absorbed. Beta and gamma radiation can travel further through air. A thin sheet of paper or 20 cm of air can absorb alpha radiation. Beta radiation can be absorbed by 3 or 4 cm of aluminium, but gamma requires several centimetres of lead to absorb most of its energy.

IONISATION

Atoms usually have the same number of protons and electrons, so an atom has no overall charge – it is neutral. Ionisation occurs when an atom gains an electron to give it an overall negative charge or when an atom loses an electron to give it an overall positive charge.

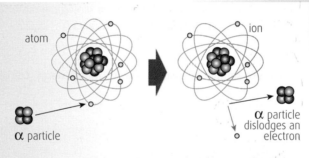

Ionisation of an atom caused by alpha radiation

Alpha radiation causes the most ionisation. This happens when an alpha particle collides with an atom removing an electron. The atom then becomes an **ion** (a charged particle).

Beta particles cause less ionisation than alpha as they are smaller particles. Gamma radiation causes even less ionisation but, because it is a wave of energy, it can travel through atoms without being absorbed.

Unexpected ionisation can be dangerous, and should be prevented. However, controlled use of ionising radiation can be beneficial:

- in the diagnosis and treatment of certain illnesses
- for protecting people, for example by its use in smoke detectors
- in industry, for example to monitor the thickness of newspaper in a paper mill.

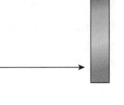

VIDEO LINK

Check out the 'Harmful Effects of Radiation' clip at www.brightredbooks.net/N5Physics

DON'T FORGET

Ionisation is when nuclear radiation changes atoms into ions.

DON'T FORGET

Although gamma radiation travels the furthest and is the most penetrating radiation, alpha radiation does the most damage over a very short distance because of its strong ionising capability.

ONLINE TEST

Take the 'Nuclear Radiation' test at www.brightredbooks.net/N5Physics

THINGS TO DO AND THINK ABOUT

Ionisation caused by radiation can be helpful, but may also be dangerous. Carry out research to find particular examples where ionisation has caused:

1. major problems and what impact these have had on the people affected by it (you could research the Chernobyl nuclear reactor disaster, for example)

2. benefits to society (perhaps you could research how smoke detectors have reduced the number of deaths and injury due to fire).

NUCLEAR RADIATION 2

The key concepts to learn in this topic are:

- the use of appropriate relationships to solve problems involving absorbed dose, equivalent dose, energy, mass and radiation weighting factor
- the use of an appropriate relationship to solve problems involving equivalent dose rate, equivalent dose and time

- knowledge of background radiation sources
- a comparison of equivalent dose due to a variety of natural and artificial sources
- awareness of equivalent dose rate and exposure safety limits for the public and for workers in radiation industries in terms of annual effective equivalent dose.

DON'T FORGET +

Radiation weighting factors (w_R) for different types of radiation are given in the Data sheet.

MEASURING THE EFFECT OF RADIATION

Absorbed dose, D

Absorbed dose

$$D = \frac{E}{m}$$

The absorbed dose is how much energy, E, per kilogram from radiation has been received. It depends on the mass, m, of biological material exposed to the radiation, and the absorbed dose is measured in **grays** (Gy).

EXAMPLE 1

A 2·5 kg sample of tissue receives 2 mJ of energy. Calculate the absorbed dose.

$$D = \frac{E}{m} = \frac{2 \times 10^{-3}}{2 \cdot 5}$$
$$= 8 \times 10^{-4} \text{ Gy} = 0 \cdot 8 \text{ mGy}$$

Equivalent dose, H

Equivalent dose

$$H = D w_R$$

The effect of radiation on humans depends on the *absorbed dose* and the *type* of radiation. Equivalent dose measures this in **sieverts** (Sv). Different types of radiation are given a **radiation weighting factor** (w_R) depending on how harmful the effect is on biological material like bone or tissue.

EXAMPLE 2

A sample of tissue which received an absorbed dose of 80 µGy was exposed to alpha radiation. Alpha radiation has a radiation weighting factor of 20. Calculate the equivalent dose.

$$H = D w_R = 80 \times 10^{-6} \times 20$$
$$= 1 \cdot 6 \times 10^{-3} \text{ Sv} = 1 \cdot 6 \text{ mSv}$$

Equivalent dose rate, $\dot{H}$

DON'T FORGET +

Absorbed dose is given in Gy, equivalent dose in Sv and equivalent dose rate in Sv h⁻¹.

For safety, it is important to monitor the *rate* at which radiation is absorbed by people who work with radiation. This helps to prevent too much exposure in a short time.

This is known as the **equivalent dose rate** ($\dot{H}$)

$$\dot{H} = \frac{H}{t}$$

Equivalent dose rate can be quoted in a variety of units including sieverts, millisieverts or microsieverts per unit time, such as second, minute or hour, for example $Sv\,h^{-1}$, $mSv\,h^{-1}$ and $\mu Sv\,h^{-1}$.

contd

EXAMPLE 3

A worker in the nuclear industry received an equivalent dose of 0·02 µSv in 12 hours. Calculate the equivalent dose rate.

$\dot{H} = \dfrac{H}{t} = \dfrac{0 \cdot 02 \times 10^{-6}}{12} = 1 \cdot 7 \times 10^{-9}$ Svh⁻¹ (Use the same units for time as given in the question.)

BACKGROUND RADIATION

When radioactive materials decay, they give out alpha or beta or gamma radiation. Radioactive materials exist everywhere, so there is always radiation around us. This is called **background radiation**.

Background radiation can be measured locally, and the amount varies according to geographic location. Different parts of the country can have slightly higher levels of background radiation.

The *average annual effective dose* that a person in the UK receives due to natural sources (such as cosmic, terrestrial and internal radiation) is approximately 2 mSv.

Artificial Source	Annual equivalent dose	
	µSv	mSv
Medical uses (X-rays)	250	0·250
Weapons testing	10	0·010
Nuclear industry (waste)	2	0·002
Other (job, TV, flights)	18	0·018
Total man-made sources	280	0·280

Natural Source	Annual equivalent dose	
	µSv	mSv
Radioactive gases in air and buildings (radon and thoron)	800	0·80
Rocks of the earth	400	0·40
In food and our bodies	370	0·37
Cosmic rays from space	300	0·30
Total natural sources	1870	1·87

The pie charts' tables show the annual equivalent dose of radiation received due to artificial and natural sources of radiation

SAFETY AND RADIATION

Annual effective dose limits

Annual effective dose limits have been set for exposure to radiation for the general public and there are higher limits for workers in certain occupations.

The annual limits are:

- 1 mSv per year for the public
- 20 mSv per year for radiation workers.

These limits are in *addition* to background radiation.

SHIELDING OF RADIATION

One of the simplest methods of reducing equivalent dose rate from ionising radiation is by **shielding**, that is placing an absorbing material in the path of the radiation. Aluminium, lead, concrete of different thicknesses and water have all been used to absorb radiation. Medical radiologists wear lead aprons.

Increasing the distance from the source can also reduce the equivalent dose rate from ionising radiations.

Shielding

 DON'T FORGET

Protection from radiation is achieved by distance and shielding from source.

VIDEO LINK

Check out the clip 'Measuring radiation background with Terra-P' at www.brightredbooks.net/N5Physics

 THINGS TO DO AND THINK ABOUT

There are a variety of tasks that can be carried out, either on your own or in a group, to explore this topic further. Why not have a go at these tasks?

1. Research the extraction of naturally occurring radioactive materials.

2. Determine the level of background radiation in a variety of places near you.

3. Debate the risks and benefits of radioactivity to society. One group could argue for the continued use of radioactive substances and another against.

NUCLEAR RADIATION 3

The key concept to learn in this topic is:
- the applications of nuclear radiation.

ONLINE

For more details on the key concept of this topic, go to www.brightredbooks.net/N5Physics

APPLICATIONS OF NUCLEAR RADIATION

Radioactive materials are in widespread use for a variety of beneficial reasons. To protect people from harmful exposure, any dangers associated with the use of radioactive materials must be considered and safeguards have to be put into place. Applications can be divided into two categories:

1. medical use   2. industrial use.

MEDICAL APPLICATIONS OF NUCLEAR RADIATION

Medical research constantly gives rise to new uses of radiation that are adopted throughout the world. Medical applications can also be divided into two categories:

1. identification (diagnosis) of health problems   2. health improvement (treatment)

Medical diagnosis

A radioactive **tracer** is a liquid isotope that is injected into a patient. Tracers can be used to check the function and health of various organs of the body.

In the case of a bone scan, a tracer travels through the blood and collects in the bones. The radiation emitted by the tracer is detected by a **gamma camera**.

The tracer collects in areas where there is a lot of **activity** in the bones. This activity could be caused by a broken bone under repair, an infection, arthritis or sometimes by cancer in the bones. These areas of increased activity (called 'hot spots' by doctors) are detected by the gamma camera. The images from the camera are analysed by computer and displayed on screens to allow doctors to identify any problems.

Gamma radiation is used for bone scans

Facts about medical tracers

- Tracers must emit gamma radiation – alpha or beta radiation would not penetrate the body to reach the gamma camera outside.
- Any isotope used as a tracer must have a short half-life (see page 54); the activity (see page 54) of the radionuclide must reduce over a short time period so that it does not remain active inside the body for too long (just long enough to permit diagnosis).
- The equivalent dose of the radiation should not be dangerous. (A normal bone scan has the same effect as about 200 X-rays, which doctors consider is not a dangerous amount for this procedure.)
- To produce the tracer, a radioactive substance (called a radionuclide) is attached to a chemical that naturally collects in a particular area of the body. This allows different organs of the body to be targeted for investigation (for example, different chemicals can be labelled to allow doctors to assess the brain, lungs, thyroid gland and kidneys).
- A common radionuclide used in tracers is technetium-99m. This is produced in nuclear reactors.

Medical treatment

External beam radiotherapy is used in the treatment of cancer to destroy cancer cells. Radiotherapy treatment is provided by a machine which emits beams of gamma radiation. The gamma radiation *kills* cancer cells but only *damages* healthy cells, which are then able to recover.

ONLINE

For more information about this, check the 'Radiation Therapy for Cancer' link at www.brightredbooks.net/N5Physics

contd

During treatment, the machine containing the gamma source can be rotated around the patient. This directs beams from many angles to target the tumour very precisely. The precision of the instrument means that the surrounding tissue is not exposed to the same large dosage of gamma radiation as the tumour.

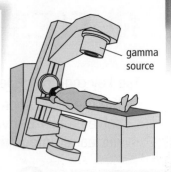

Facts about radiotherapy

- The radioactive source commonly used to emit gamma radiation is cobalt-60.
- Cobalt-60 is sometimes produced in nuclear reactors or linear accelerators.
- Other types of radiation used in radiotherapy include high energy X-rays, protons and electrons.

Treatment with gamma radiation

INDUSTRIAL APPLICATIONS OF NUCLEAR RADIATION

Many industries routinely use radioactive materials to improve production. It is important to detect the amount of radiation in a workplace that uses radioactive materials, to monitor employees' exposure. The safety and protection of employees and of the general public during the use of nuclear radiation is controlled and monitored by the government.

Film badges

When working regularly with radioactive sources, employees sometimes wear **film badges**. These badges contain photographic film that darkens when exposed to radiation of all kinds. (Visible light cannot reach the film.) A simplified badge is shown in the diagram.

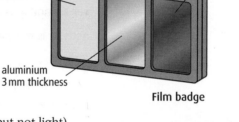

Film badge

This badge has three windows:

1. The uncovered window allows all nuclear radiations to pass through (but not light).
2. The thin aluminium absorbs alpha radiation, so beta and gamma radiation would reach the film.
3. The thin lead window absorbs alpha and beta radiation, so only gamma radiation would penetrate.

By analysing where the film has darkened, exposure to different types of radiation can be identified. The amount of darkening of the film also indicates the amount of the radiation received.

ONLINE TEST

Take the 'Nuclear Radiation' test at www.brightredbooks. net/N5Physics

Inspecting welds

Heavy duty welding to join two pieces of thick steel is common in many industries and it is used in tasks from joining oil pipes to building ships. It is important to be able to check any welded joint for flaws which could cause failure. Air bubbles and other weaknesses are common problems.

A gamma source is placed on one side of the welded joint. A detector on the other side picks up differences in the radiation level caused by the presence of air bubbles or other weaknesses.

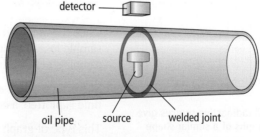

Using a gamma radiation source to inspect a weld

THINGS TO DO AND THINK ABOUT

1. Research the internet to find out about other medical and industrial uses of radiation. Possible examples are: sterilising medical instruments, sterilising food, controlling the thickness of vinyl flooring during production, smoke detectors and radioactive dating of ancient objects.

2. Present your findings to the rest of your group.

NUCLEAR RADIATION 4

The key concepts to learn in this topic are:

- the use of an appropriate relationship to solve problems involving activity, number of nuclear disintegrations and time

- the definition of *half-life*
- the use of graphical or numerical data to determine the half-life of a radioactive material.

ONLINE

For more details on the key concepts of this topic, go to www.brightredbooks.net/N5Physics

ACTIVITY

When a radioactive substance emits radiation, the nuclei of the atoms decay.

The rate of decay is called the **activity** of the substance.

$$\text{Activity} = \frac{\text{number of nuclei decaying}}{\text{time}}$$

$$A = \frac{N}{t}$$

So, the activity of a radioactive source is the number of decays per second.

Activity is measured in **becquerels** (Bq). One becquerel is one decay per second.

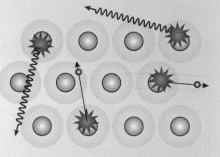

Radioactive decay

EXAMPLE 1

The activity of 1 g of uranium is 4·22 MBq. How many decays will occur in 1 minute?

$A = \frac{N}{t}$ so $4\cdot22 \times 10^6 = \frac{N}{60}$ (Converting 1 minute into seconds)

$N = 2\cdot53 \times 10^8$ decays

Radioactive decay is a random process – a radioactive substance contains many nuclei of atoms which decay at random. It is impossible to predict *when* the nucleus of an individual atom will decay but, because there are so many nuclei in even a small sample, we can predict the *average number* that will decay in a certain time. Some sources take billions of years to decay while others remain active for only fractions of a second.

DON'T FORGET

Activity is the number of atomic decays every second, expressed in becquerels (Bq).

HALF-LIFE

Once the atoms in a sample start to decay, there are fewer atoms left to decay. The sample loses *half* its activity after a certain time. This time is known as its half-life. The sample's activity drops by half after each further half-life time.

So, the activity of a radioactive source decreases with time. If a graph of activity against time is plotted, a curve like that shown in the diagram to the left is obtained.

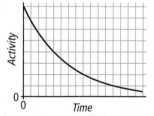

All radioactive sources give graphs of a similar shape

DON'T FORGET

The time taken for the activity of a substance to halve is called the half-life.

This type of graph can be used to determine the half-life of the radioactive source. The time for the activity to fall from one value to *half* of that value is obtained using values from the graph, as shown in the diagram to the right.

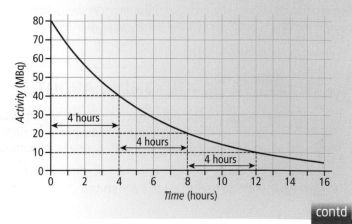

contd

Using the graph, the time for activity to fall from 80–40 MBq is 4 hours. The same time is obtained between 20–10 MBq. The half-life of the source is 4 hours.

EXAMPLE 2

A Geiger Muller tube connected to a counter is used to measure the counts per minute of a radioactive source every hour for 20 hours (see diagram).

The radioactive source is placed in a lead container to remove the effect of background radiation. Only readings from the source are detected. The results are recorded in a table.

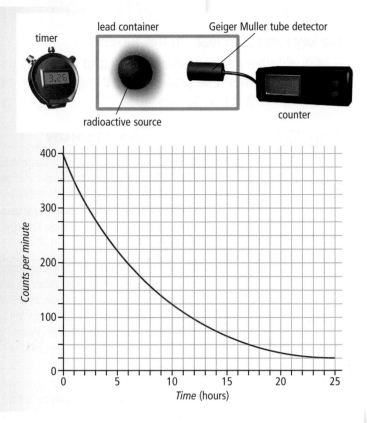

Counts per minute	400	250	160	95	60	33
Time (hours)	0	4	8	12	16	20

A graph of count rate per minute against time is drawn.

Determine the half-life of the source from the graph.

From the graph, the count rate per minute falls from 400 to 200 in 6 hours.

So half-life is 6 hours.

Half-life can also be calculated from information which does not include a graph or table of results.

EXAMPLE 3

The activity of a radioisotope used in a hospital was 160 kBq at 6 am on 3rd February. At 6 am on 5th February, its activity was 10 kBq. Calculate the half-life of the radioisotope.

First calculate the number of half-lives needed to get from 160 kBq to 10 Bq.

$160 \rightarrow 80 \rightarrow 40 \rightarrow 20 \rightarrow 10$

This is four halving processes, so four half-lives. From 6 am on 3rd Feb to 6 am on 5th Feb is 48 hours. So there have been four half-lives in 48 hours.

Half-life $= \dfrac{48}{4} = 12$ hours

The half-lives of radioactive substances range from a few milliseconds to billions of years.

THINGS TO DO AND THINK ABOUT

1. Investigate, either individually or as members of a group, the half-life of the radioactive fuel used in nuclear power stations.

2. Find out what happens to this fuel when it is 'spent'. What are the advantages and disadvantages of using nuclear energy to produce electricity compared to other forms of energy production (such as coal-fired power stations)?

3. Present your findings to the group and discuss the benefits and problems.

4. Debate these arguments to explore questions about world energy shortages, pollution, global warming and public safety, for example.

DON'T FORGET

When using a graph to determine half-life, choose values which are easy to read.

ONLINE TEST

Take the 'Nuclear Radiation' test at www.brightredbooks.net/N5Physics

ONLINE

For more on this, check out the 'Half-Life' link at www.brightredbooks.net/N5Physics

NUCLEAR RADIATION 5

The key concept to learn in this topic is:

- a qualitative description of fission and fusion, with emphasis on the importance of these processes in the generation of energy.

DON'T FORGET

Energy is released in nuclear fission reactions.

NUCLEAR FISSION

In **fission**, a nucleus with a large mass number (and so a large number of protons and neutrons in its nucleus) splits into two nuclei of smaller mass numbers, usually with the release of neutrons. Energy is also released.

The amount of energy produced can be huge if a large enough number of atoms are allowed to split in a short time. When atoms of elements like uranium and plutonium split, two entirely different elements are produced, each with smaller atomic masses.

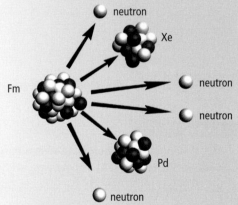

large atom splits into two smaller atoms

energy released

The large atom splits into two atoms of two different elements

Spontaneous fission

The fission, or decay, of the atoms may be spontaneous. This random nature means that the fission events cannot be reliably predicted.

Spontaneous fission of fermium Fm atoms produces smaller atoms of palladium Pd and xenon Xe, and four neutrons are liberated in the process.

Induced fission

Large atoms can be forced to split, by bombarding them with slow moving neutrons. This process is known as *induced* fission.

In this example of a fission reaction, a uranium U atom is bombarded by a slow neutron, which causes it to split and release energy. Two new smaller atoms of the elements barium Ba and krypton Kr are produced. Three neutrons are also released.

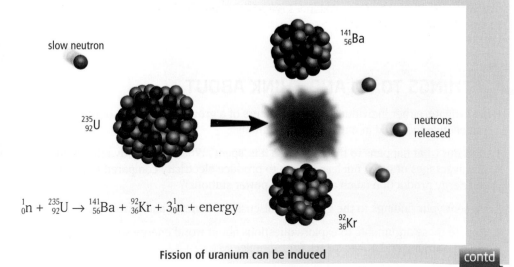

$$^{1}_{0}n + ^{235}_{92}U \rightarrow ^{141}_{56}Ba + ^{92}_{36}Kr + 3^{1}_{0}n + energy$$

Fission of uranium can be induced

contd

The new elements produced as a result of nuclear fission can vary depending on which large element is used and the initial conditions before the fission.

In a controlled process, the neutrons released in each fission process can be used to bombard further large atoms. These also split, releasing more energy and neutrons. This is called a **chain reaction**.

The energy released by these fission reactions can be very large. It can be removed from the radioactive mass to provide a huge source of energy. Induced fission is used in the reactors of nuclear power stations to provide energy. The energy is used to heat water to produce steam which is used in the generation of electricity.

NUCLEAR FUSION

Fusion is the joining of nuclei.

In fusion, two nuclei combine to form a nucleus of larger mass number. The nuclei that fuse together are usually very small.

A large amount of energy is released, and no radioactive waste is produced in the reaction.

There is a virtually unlimited amount of the isotopes of hydrogen needed for fusion in seawater, and no greenhouse gases are emitted.

$$^2_1H + {}^3_1H \rightarrow {}^4_2He + {}^1_0n + energy$$

deuterium

helium

energy

tritium

neutron

Fusion is the energy source of the Sun and the stars, but physicists are still working on the design of nuclear-fusion reactors for Earth!

DON'T FORGET

Fission = splitting, fusion = joining.

ONLINE TEST

Take the 'Nuclear Radiation' test at www.brightredbooks. net/N5Physics

ONLINE

Have a look at the 'Culham Centre for Fusion Energy' link to learn more at www.brightredbooks.net/ N5Physics

THINGS TO DO AND THINK ABOUT

1. Nuclear fission: carry out research into chain reactions. What use is made of this phenomenon in the modern world? Debate the advantages and disadvantages of nuclear fission to society.

2. Nuclear fusion:

   (a) Carry out research to find out what happens when nuclear fusion runs out in stars.

   (b) Find out what problems there are on Earth which have so far prevented the production of energy by nuclear fusion.

VELOCITY AND DISPLACEMENT 1

The key concepts to learn in this topic are:

- the definition of vector and scalar quantities
- the identification of force, speed, velocity, distance, displacement, acceleration, mass, time and energy as vector or scalar quantities
- the calculation of the resultant of two vector quantities in one dimension
- the use of appropriate relationships to solve problems involving velocity, displacement and time.

Temperature is defined by value and unit

Vector quantities:

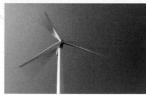

velocity

force

weight

DON'T FORGET

You should know which quantities are scalars and which are vectors.

ONLINE

For a whole lot more on scalars and vectors, have a look at 'Describing Motion with Words' at www.brightredbooks.net/N5Physics

SCALARS AND VECTORS

Physical quantities are studied in physics. Physical quantities can be classified as one of two types:

- scalar quantities
- vector quantities

It is important to be able to identify scalar and vector quantities.

Scalar quantity

Scalar quantities:

distance   time   mass

A scalar quantity is defined by its *magnitude* alone. This means that it only has size. Scalar quantities can be added or subtracted using basic arithmetic. For example, the temperature of an object is a quantity which has a value and a unit (°C). This information is all that is required to define this quantity.

Vector quantity

A vector quantity is defined by both its *magnitude* and its *direction*. This means that for a vector both size and direction must be stated. For example, the direction could be up or down, left or right, or the direction of a compass bearing such as north east (NE) or south (S).

Vectors *cannot* usually be simply added or subtracted; the direction is important and has to be taken into account. To add vectors together, we have to use scale diagrams or mathematical formulae, such as trigonometry and Pythagoras' theorem.

Some scalar and vector quantities used in this course are shown in the tables below.

Scalars	Symbol	Unit
distance	d	m
speed	v	ms^{-1}
time	t	s
mass	m	kg
energy	E	J
power	P	W
temperature	T	°C
work	E_w	J

Vectors	Symbol	Unit
displacement	s	m
velocity	v	ms^{-1}
acceleration	a	ms^{-2}
force	F	N
weight	W	N

DISTANCE AND DISPLACEMENT

Distance

Distance is a scalar quantity. The symbol for distance is d. Distance is defined by a number and its unit, the metre, m. For example, 'the length of the school laboratory is 8 m'.

contd

Displacement

Displacement is a vector quantity. The symbol for displacement is *s*. Displacement is the direct distance travelled in a stated direction from the starting point. For example, 'an explorer walks 20 km due north from the base camp'.

EXAMPLE 1

A student travels 10 m east along a straight corridor and is sent back 7 m for running.

(a) What is the distance travelled by the student?

Total distance travelled, d = 10 + 7 = 17 m

(b) What is the displacement of the student from the starting point?

Displacement is 10 + (–7) = 3 m east

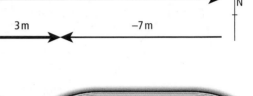

EXAMPLE 2

A runner goes round a race track three times. The track has a length of 220 m.

(a) Calculate the distance travelled by the runner.

Distance travelled, d = 3 × 220 = 660 m

(b) Determine the final displacement of the runner from the starting point.

Displacement, s = 0 m (since the runner finished 0 m from the start line)

Speed

Speed and average speed are scalar quantities. The symbol for speed is *v* and the symbol for average speed is $\bar{v}$. Speed is the distance travelled by an object per unit of time. The unit for speed is metres per second, m s^{-1}. Speed does not have a direction.

The relationships used to calculate speed and average speed are: $v = \dfrac{d}{t}$ and $\bar{v} = \dfrac{d}{t}$

Where: v = speed $\bar{v}$ = average speed d = distance travelled
t = time taken to travel this distance.

Velocity

Velocity and average velocity are vector quantities. The symbol for velocity is *v* and the symbol for average velocity is $\bar{v}$. Velocity is the displacement of an object per unit of time including the direction of the object with respect to its starting position.

The relationships used to calculate velocity and average velocity are: $v = \dfrac{s}{t}$ and $\bar{v} = \dfrac{s}{t}$

Where: v = velocity $\bar{v}$ = average velocity
s = displacement from starting position
t = time taken to travel this displacement.

The unit for velocity is metres per second, m s^{-1}, and the displacement is described using a three-figure bearing or by giving direction points of the compass. For example, the velocity of the bus was 18 m s^{-1} at a bearing of 315 (or N 45° W).

THINGS TO DO AND THINK ABOUT

1. Find the displacement of your house from your school or college. What information do you need? You may find it helpful to use a map of the local area to measure directions and distance. Remember, the displacement requires a direction as well as the actual distance.

2. Use the time it takes for you to reach school to calculate average speed and average velocity.

VELOCITY AND DISPLACEMENT 2

The key concepts to learn in this topic are:

- the calculation of the resultant of two vector quantities in one dimension or at right angles
- the determination of displacement and/or distance using scale diagram or calculation.

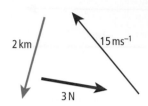

2 km   15 ms⁻¹

3 N

Vectors (not to scale)

COMBINING VECTORS

Vectors can be represented by a straight line with an arrowhead. The size of the vector is represented by the length of the line. The direction of the vector is represented by the direction of the arrow.

Vectors can be added or combined to give a single vector which is known as the *resultant* vector. When more than one single vector acts in the same straight line (or in one dimension) they can be added algebraically.

EXAMPLE 1

A space rocket has a weight of 15 000 N. At lift-off, the engine force is 25 000 N. Calculate the resultant force.

The forces are vectors:
- the weight (15 000 N) acts downwards
- the engine force (25 000 N) acts upwards.

Resultant force = 25 000 – 15 000 = 10 000 N upwards

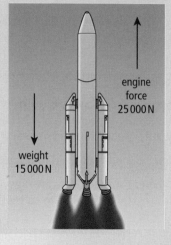

engine force
25 000 N

weight
15 000 N

Stating the direction of the resultant

The direction of the resultant should be stated in the same terms as the original information. For example, in Example 1, the force vectors clearly act upwards or downwards. When compass directions are given, the direction can be stated as a three-figure bearing or as a compass bearing.

When there is an angle between the single vectors, then a scale drawing or mathematical calculation (using Pythagoras' theorem and trigonometry) has to be used to determine the resultant.

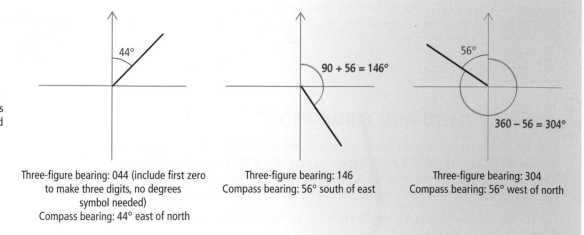

This is how the north direction is usually indicated on diagrams

Three-figure bearing: 044 (include first zero to make three digits, no degrees symbol needed)
Compass bearing: 44° east of north

Three-figure bearing: 146
Compass bearing: 56° south of east

Three-figure bearing: 304
Compass bearing: 56° west of north

Direction expressed as equivalent three-figure bearings and compass bearings

contd

EXAMPLE 2

A helicopter is travelling at a velocity of 48 ms⁻¹ due east and then encounters a crosswind of 12 ms⁻¹ due south. By scale diagram, or otherwise, determine the resultant velocity of the aircraft.

Solutions by scale diagram and trigonometry are given to this problem below.

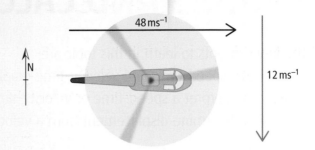

How to solve problems by scale diagram

- Choose and write down a scale to represent the velocities.
- Draw the direction indicating north.
- Using a ruler, draw the vectors according to the chosen scale.
- Add vectors 'head to tail'.
- Draw the resultant from start to finish.
- Measure the length of the resultant.
- Use the scale to convert back to velocity.
- Measure the angle of the resultant.
- State this as a three-figure bearing.

You will need this equipment to draw scale diagrams

VIDEO LINK

Check out the 'Vectors' link at www.brightredbooks.net/N5Physics

Solving Example 2 by scale drawing method

Resultant length
= 12·4 cm
→ 12·4 × 4 = 49·6 ms⁻¹

Resultant angle = 14°,
so three-figure bearing
is 90 + 14 = 104

scale: 1 cm represents 4 ms⁻¹

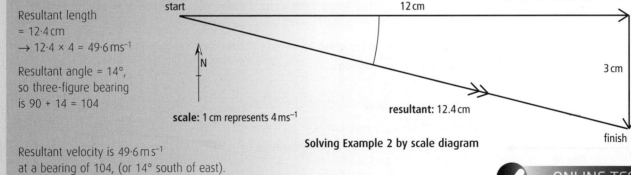

Solving Example 2 by scale diagram

Resultant velocity is 49·6 ms⁻¹
at a bearing of 104, (or 14° south of east).

How to solve problems using Pythagoras' theorem and trigonometry

ONLINE TEST

How well have you learned about scalars and vectors? Take the 'Velocity and displacement' test at www.brightredbooks.net/N5Physics

Solving Example 2 Using Pythagoras' theorem and trigonometry:

$x^2 = y^2 + z^2$

$x^2 = 48^2 + 12^2 = 2448$

$x = 49 \cdot 5 \, ms^{-1}$

$\tan\theta = \dfrac{12}{48} \quad \theta = 14°$

Vector sketch

The resultant velocity is 49·5 ms⁻¹ at a bearing of 104, (or 14° south of east).

⚠ THINGS TO DO AND THINK ABOUT

1. Investigate the sport of orienteering. Find out how the contestants navigate their way around the course.

2. What is the importance of vectors in this sport?

GRAPHS AND CALCULATIONS 1

The key concepts to learn in this topic are:

- to sketch speed–time and velocity–time graphs for objects from recorded or experimental data
- how to interpret a speed–time or velocity–time graph to describe the motion of an object
- how to determine displacement from a velocity–time graph.

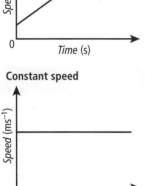

Constantly increasing speed

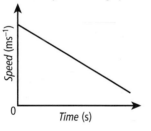

Constant speed

Constantly decreasing speed

Different types of motion represented by speed–time graphs

SPEED–TIME GRAPHS

Speed–time graphs are often used to display motion, which often is not in a straight line.

Uniform **acceleration** means that the object's speed increases by the same amount each second or decreases by the same amount each second (sometimes called **deceleration**).

EXAMPLE 1

The diagram shows a speed–time graph for a Formula 1 car completing part of one lap of a racetrack.

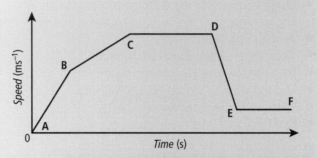

A Formula 1 racetrack has right and left turns and long, straight stretches of track. So, the driver has to change the direction of the car many times during one lap. The car speeds up, slows down, and sometimes travels at constant speed.

Use the letters on the graph to identify the section(s) which illustrate:

(a) positive acceleration
A–B and B–C

(b) constant speed
C–D and E–F

(c) negative acceleration (deceleration).
D–E

EXAMPLE 2

Which of the following speed–time graphs represents the motion of a vehicle that accelerates from rest, then moves at constant speed, then accelerates again, then decelerates to rest?

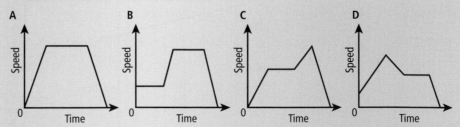

C is the correct answer. A shows only one acceleration. B starts at a constant speed, not from rest. D has two decelerations.

When drawing a speed–time graph, always label the origin of each axis with zero and choose scales carefully to produce a graph which is a reasonable size. Remember to label each axis with its name and the unit.

contd

DON'T FORGET

The shape of a speed-time graph describes the object's motion.

EXAMPLE 3

A metro train is at rest at station A. The train accelerates uniformly from rest to a speed of $35\,ms^{-1}$ in 25 s. It continues at this speed for 45 s, passing through station B without stopping. The driver then applies the brakes for 20 s, bringing the train to a stop at the end of the line, station C, where it waits for 20 s. The train then returns in the opposite direction. It accelerates uniformly from rest to reach a speed of $30\,ms^{-1}$ in 20 s. The driver then applies the brakes for 15 s to stop at station B.

Draw the speed–time graph of the train.

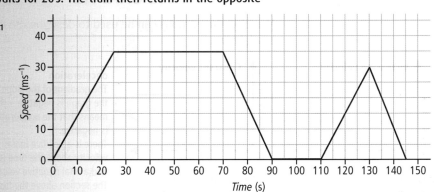

EXAMPLE 4

The speed of a trolley is recorded at regular intervals as it moves down a runway. The first part of the runway is steeper than the second part.

The results are recorded in the table.

Speed (ms^{-1})	0·3	0·6	0·9	1·2	1·5	1·8	2·1	2·2	2·3	2·4
Time (s)	0·1	0·2	0·3	0·4	0·5	0·6	0·7	0·8	0·9	1·0

(a) Draw a speed–time graph of the results.
See graph opposite.

(b) Describe the shape of the graph.
The graph has two different accelerations, greater at the start than at the end. This is seen from the different gradients of the graph – the first section has a steeper gradient, which indicates a greater acceleration.

(c) Explain the shape of the graph.
The slope of the second part of the runway is less steep than the first part. The trolley will have a smaller acceleration on this part of the slope.

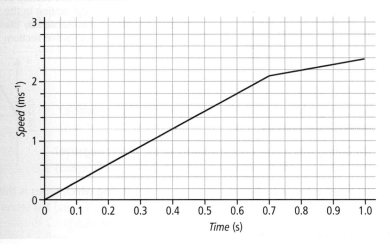

THINGS TO DO AND THINK ABOUT

During maintenance work on motorways, the speed of vehicles is usually restricted. Average speed cameras can be used to control traffic speed. Investigate how this process works.

1. How is the car recognised, timed and the average speed calculated? Is it a successful method of speed control?

2. Can cars 'dodge' the process by travelling very fast on some stretches and going very slow on other parts of the restricted stretch of road?

ACCELERATION

The key concepts to learn in this topic are:

- the use of an appropriate relationship to solve problems involving acceleration, initial velocity (or speed), final velocity (or speed) and time
- the determination of acceleration from a velocity–time graph.

DON'T FORGET

Only uniform acceleration will be considered in this course.

A PRECISE DEFINITION

Acceleration is defined as the *rate of change of velocity in unit time*. For example, a car which accelerates from rest has uniform (or constant) acceleration when its velocity increases by the same amount each second.

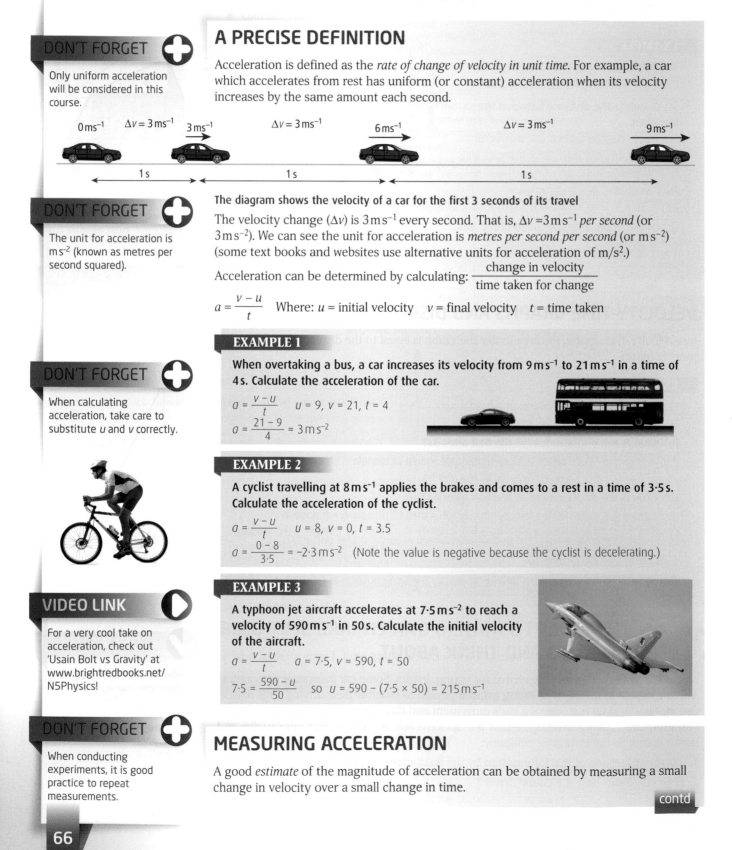

$0\,\text{ms}^{-1}$ $\Delta v = 3\,\text{ms}^{-1}$ $3\,\text{ms}^{-1}$ $\Delta v = 3\,\text{ms}^{-1}$ $6\,\text{ms}^{-1}$ $\Delta v = 3\,\text{ms}^{-1}$ $9\,\text{ms}^{-1}$

1 s   1 s   1 s

DON'T FORGET

The unit for acceleration is ms^{-2} (known as metres per second squared).

The diagram shows the velocity of a car for the first 3 seconds of its travel

The velocity change (Δv) is $3\,\text{ms}^{-1}$ every second. That is, $\Delta v = 3\,\text{ms}^{-1}$ *per second* (or $3\,\text{ms}^{-2}$). We can see the unit for acceleration is *metres per second per second* (or ms^{-2}) (some text books and websites use alternative units for acceleration of m/s².)

Acceleration can be determined by calculating: $\dfrac{\text{change in velocity}}{\text{time taken for change}}$

$$a = \frac{v - u}{t}$$ Where: u = initial velocity v = final velocity t = time taken

EXAMPLE 1

When overtaking a bus, a car increases its velocity from $9\,\text{ms}^{-1}$ to $21\,\text{ms}^{-1}$ in a time of $4\,\text{s}$. Calculate the acceleration of the car.

$a = \dfrac{v - u}{t}$ $u = 9, v = 21, t = 4$

$a = \dfrac{21 - 9}{4} = 3\,\text{ms}^{-2}$

DON'T FORGET

When calculating acceleration, take care to substitute u and v correctly.

EXAMPLE 2

A cyclist travelling at $8\,\text{ms}^{-1}$ applies the brakes and comes to a rest in a time of $3{\cdot}5\,\text{s}$. Calculate the acceleration of the cyclist.

$a = \dfrac{v - u}{t}$ $u = 8, v = 0, t = 3.5$

$a = \dfrac{0 - 8}{3{\cdot}5} = -2{\cdot}3\,\text{ms}^{-2}$ (Note the value is negative because the cyclist is decelerating.)

EXAMPLE 3

A typhoon jet aircraft accelerates at $7{\cdot}5\,\text{ms}^{-2}$ to reach a velocity of $590\,\text{ms}^{-1}$ in $50\,\text{s}$. Calculate the initial velocity of the aircraft.

$a = \dfrac{v - u}{t}$ $a = 7{\cdot}5, v = 590, t = 50$

$7{\cdot}5 = \dfrac{590 - u}{50}$ so $u = 590 - (7{\cdot}5 \times 50) = 215\,\text{ms}^{-1}$

VIDEO LINK

For a very cool take on acceleration, check out 'Usain Bolt vs Gravity' at www.brightredbooks.net/N5Physics!

DON'T FORGET

When conducting experiments, it is good practice to repeat measurements.

MEASURING ACCELERATION

A good *estimate* of the magnitude of acceleration can be obtained by measuring a small change in velocity over a small change in time.

contd

Consider a trolley with two cards of equal width attached to it. The trolley is released from the top of a slope and each card, in turn, passes through a light gate near the foot of the slope.

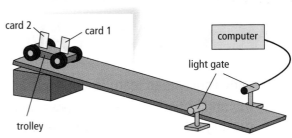

- Times t_1 and t_2 for card 1 and card 2 to pass through the light gate are measured.
- The time t_3 – the time between card 1 and card 2 passing through the light gate is also measured.
- The initial speed u is calculated using the card width and the time t_1.
- The final speed v is calculated using the card width and the time t_2.
- The acceleration of the trolley is calculated using: $a = \dfrac{v - u}{t}$

Investigating acceleration

Sample results

Card width $d = 0.05\,m$

Time for card 1, $t_1 = 0.15\,s$ $\quad u = \dfrac{\text{card width}}{t_1} = 0.33\,ms^{-1}$

Time for card 2, $t_1 = 0.08\,s$ $\quad v = \dfrac{\text{card width}}{t_1} = 0.63\,ms^{-1}$

Time interval $t_3 = 0.75\,s$ $\quad a = \dfrac{v - u}{t_3} = 0.4\,ms^{-2}$

A similar method uses two light gates and one card length to calculate the average acceleration.

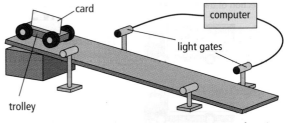

Investigating average acceleration

ACCELERATION FROM VELOCITY-TIME GRAPHS

The gradient of a velocity–time graph is equal to the acceleration.

The equation $a = \dfrac{v - u}{t}$ can be used to calculate the gradient of the graph and hence the acceleration.

Care is needed when selecting values for u, v, and t from the graph. For this graph,

$\text{gradient} = \dfrac{y_2 - y_1}{x_2 - x_1} = \dfrac{10 - 0}{20 - 0} = 0.5\,ms^{-2}$, so acceleration $= 0.5\,ms^{-2}$

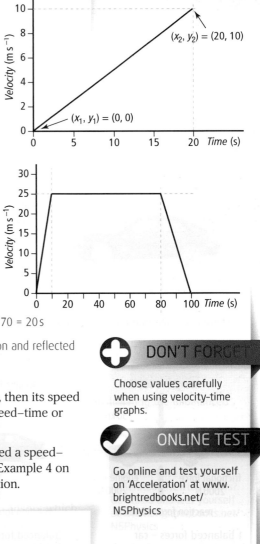

EXAMPLE 4

The graph represents the motion of a tram travelling in a straight line between two stops.

(a) Calculate the acceleration of the tram in the first 10 seconds.

Select values from the graph: $u = 0$, $v = 25$, time interval $t = 10 - 0 = 10\,s$

$a = \dfrac{v - u}{t} = \dfrac{25 - 0}{10} = 2.5\,ms^{-2}$

(b) Calculate the acceleration of the tram in the last 20 seconds.

Select values from graph: $u = 25$, $v = 0$ (tram is at rest), time interval $t = 90 - 70 = 20\,s$

$a = \dfrac{v - u}{t} = \dfrac{0 - 25}{20} = -1.25\,ms^{-2}$ (Note the negative sign, meaning deceleration and reflected in the downward slope of the graph.)

When an object is moving in a straight line and does not change direction, then its speed and velocity are *equal*. Its velocity–time graph can be labelled as either speed–time or velocity–time.

The velocity–time graph for the tram in Example 4 could have been labelled a speed–time graph, because the tram travels in one direction only. For the ball in Example 4 on p65 only a velocity–time graph is possible because the ball changes direction.

DON'T FORGET

Choose values carefully when using velocity-time graphs.

ONLINE TEST

Go online and test yourself on 'Acceleration' at www.brightredbooks.net/N5Physics

THINGS TO DO AND THINK ABOUT

1. Formula 1 racing cars must produce large acceleration. Equally, to negotiate the hairpin bends and perform overtaking measures, the cars must be capable of large deceleration. Investigate the maximum deceleration of F1 cars. Use this value to calculate the time that an F1 car would take to decelerate from $200\,kmh^{-1}$ to $20\,kmh^{-1}$.

WORK AND ENERGY

The key concepts to learn in this topic are:

- the use of an appropriate relationship to solve problems involving work done, unbalanced force and distance/displacement
- the use of an appropriate relationship to solve problems involving weight, mass and gravitational field strength, including on different planets.

ENERGY TRANSFER

Energy can be transformed from one type to another. Consider a cyclist accelerating on a level road, then freewheeling up and down a small hill, and finally braking to rest. The various energy transformations are described in the diagram.

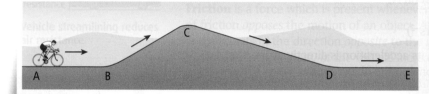

Energy transformations
A–B chemical energy to kinetic energy as cyclist accelerates from rest
B–C kinetic energy to gravitational potential energy
C–D gravitational potential energy to kinetic energy
D–E kinetic energy to heat energy as cyclist brakes and decelerates

VIDEO LINK

Check out the 'Energy Transfer' clip at www.brightredbooks.net/N5Physics

Work done

Work done is another name for the amount of energy required when a force, F, is applied to move an object over a distance, d. Work is a scalar quantity.

The relationship for work is: $E_w = Fd$,

where: E_w is the work done (in joules, J) F is the force applied (in newtons, N)
d is the distance (in metres, m).

DON'T FORGET

Work and energy have the same unit: joules.

> **EXAMPLE 1**
>
> A force of 70 N moves a wheelbarrow over a distance of 30 m. Calculate the work done.
> $E_w = Fd = 70 \times 30 = 2100\,J$

> **EXAMPLE 2**
>
> During a short journey, a metro train exerted a force of 7·5 kN and did $2\cdot5 \times 10^6$ J of work. Calculate how far the train travelled.
> $d = \dfrac{E_w}{F} = \dfrac{2\cdot5 \times 10^6}{7\cdot5 \times 10^3} = 333\,m$

> **EXAMPLE 3**
>
> A box has a weight of 65 N. It is lifted from the ground through a height of 0·5 m at a constant speed.
>
> **(a) State the minimum force required to lift the box.**
> The minimum force is 65 N. Since the box is lifted at constant speed, the upward force must balance the weight acting downwards.
>
> **(b) Calculate the work done lifting the box if its weight is 65 N.**
> $E_w = Fd = 65 \times 0\cdot5 = 32\cdot5\,J$

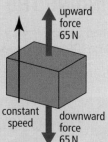

moving parts in the engine   air resistance

between the axles and wheels

Sources of friction in moving cars

In many situations, when work is done, it is to overcome a frictional force. For example, when a car is moving along a road, there are frictional forces (resistive forces) opposing the motion. The car engine has to do work *against* friction, even when travelling at constant speed.

contd

EXAMPLE 4

A 1100 kg car travelled along a 2·5 km-long road at constant speed. The car engine exerted a force of 3·5 kN.

(a) State the size of the frictional force acting on the car.

3·5 kN (Since the car moves at constant speed, the engine and friction forces are balanced.)

(b) Calculate the work done against friction.

$E_w = Fd = 3.5 \times 10^3 \times 2.5 \times 10^3 = 8.75 \times 10^6 \, J$

WEIGHT, MASS AND GRAVITATIONAL FIELD STRENGTH

The weight of an object is the force of gravity acting on the object and can be calculated using the relationship:

$W = mg$ where: W = the weight of the object in newtons (N)

m = the mass of the object in kilograms (kg)

g = the gravitational field strength (9·8 N kg^{-1} on Earth)

Gravitational field strength is defined as the *weight per unit mass* (or the force of gravity acting on each kilogram). On Earth the gravitational field strength is 9·8 N kg^{-1}.

The weight of an object decreases as it moves away from the Earth as shown by this graph.

The force of gravity is zero in deep space at distances well away from the Earth and other planets.

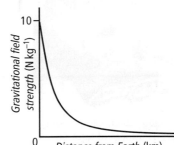

The force of gravity decreases as an object moves further away from the Earth

EXAMPLE 5

Calculate the weight of a gold bar of mass 12·7 kg stored in a bank vault.

$W = mg = 12.7 \times 9.8 = 124.5 \, N$

Different places in the solar system have different gravitational field strengths. This table appears in the exam Data sheet.

EXAMPLE 6

The weight on the surface of Mars of the Curiosity Rover robotic explorer vehicle is 3·33 ×10³ N. Calculate the mass of the vehicle.

The gravitational field strength of Mars is obtained from the Data sheet.

$m = \dfrac{W}{g} = \dfrac{3.33 \times 10^3}{3.7} = 900 \, kg$

For objects falling close to the surface of a planet, the acceleration of the falling object has the same numerical value as the gravitational field strength for the planet.

EXAMPLE 5

On which planet would a falling ball accelerate at 8·9 m s^{-2}?

Venus. (The planet Venus has gravitational field strength of 8·9 N kg^{-1})

	Gravitational field strength on the surface in N kg^{-1}
Earth	9·8
Jupiter	23
Mars	3·7
Mercury	3·7
Moon	1·6
Neptune	11
Saturn	9·0
Sun	270
Uranus	8·7
Venus	8·9

ONLINE TEST

How well have you learned about work and energy? Go online and test yourself at www.brightredbooks.net/N5Physics

THINGS TO DO AND THINK ABOUT

Car designers investigate ways to reduce frictional effects on cars when they move. If the forces of friction acting on a car as it moves can be reduced, less work needs to be done by the engine to overcome the frictional effects, requiring less energy, and so less fuel.

1. Carry out research to find out how the air frictional force is affected by the shape of the car, and how car designers investigate this.

GRAVITY, WEIGHTLESSNESS AND FREEFALL

The key concept to learn in this topic is:

- the use of **Newton's laws** to explain free-fall and terminal velocity.

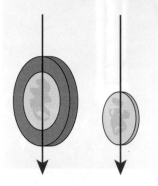

If a £2 coin and a 5p coin are dropped simultaneously from the same height they will both have an acceleration of 9·8 m s⁻² and hit the ground at the same time

DON'T FORGET

All objects have the same acceleration when falling close to the Earth's surface, if air resistance is negligible.

ACCELERATION DUE TO GRAVITY

The acceleration due to gravity on Earth is $9\cdot8\,\text{m s}^{-2}$. When an object is dropped, the only force acting on it is its weight (discounting air resistance) – this is an unbalanced force. The object will accelerate and fall freely, with the acceleration due to gravity ($9\cdot8\,\text{m s}^{-2}$).

EXAMPLE 1

Show that the acceleration of an apple of mass 0·1 kg is 9·8 m s⁻² when it falls from a tree.

Weight of apple $W = mg$
$= 0\cdot1 \times 9\cdot8 = 0\cdot98$ N

Unbalanced force on falling apple
$=$ its weight $= 0\cdot98$ N

$a = \dfrac{F}{m} = \dfrac{0\cdot98}{0\cdot1} = 9\cdot8\,\text{ms}^{-2}$

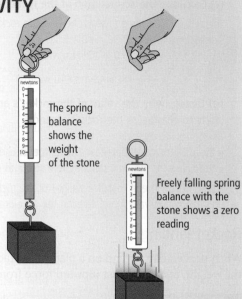

The spring balance shows the weight of the stone

Freely falling spring balance with the stone shows a zero reading

Objects in freefall appear weightless

TERMINAL VELOCITY

When an unbalanced force acts on an object, it accelerates (Newton's second law). When the forces acting on a moving object are balanced, it moves at a constant velocity (Newton's first law). **Terminal velocity** occurs when the forces acting on a moving object become *balanced*.

Consider a skydiver jumping from an aircraft. The skydiver accelerates due to his weight and his velocity increases. As the velocity *increases*, the upward air resistance force also *increases*. Eventually these two forces balance.

The skydiver then falls at constant velocity. This is known as terminal velocity. (For skydivers this velocity is about 56 m s⁻¹.) When the skydiver deploys the parachute, the area of the parachute makes the skydiver and parachute far less streamlined. The air resistance force increases rapidly.

This causes an upward force which decelerates the parachutist. Eventually the weight and air resistance forces balance again at a velocity of about 6 m s⁻¹. The skydiver now falls at a terminal velocity of 6 m s⁻¹, a safer velocity for landing than 56 m s⁻¹!

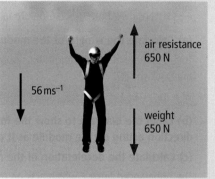

air resistance 650 N

56 m s⁻¹

weight 650 N

When velocity and air resistance balance, the skydiver falls at constant (terminal) velocity

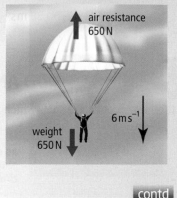

air resistance 650 N

6 m s⁻¹

weight 650 N

contd

EXAMPLE 2

A ball bearing was dropped into a jar of glycerine. The velocity of the ball bearing was measured at 0·1s time intervals, and the results recorded in the table. Use the table of results to explain the motion of the ball bearing in the glycerine.

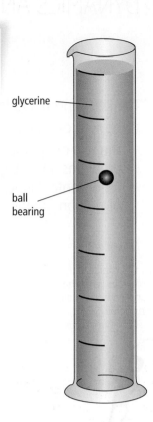

glycerine

ball bearing

Velocity (m s⁻¹)	0	0·20	0·40	0·60	0·80	0·95	1·04	1·06	1·12	1·12	1·12	1·12
Time (s)	0	0·1	0·2	0·3	0·4	0·5	0·6	0·7	0·8	1·0	1·1	1·2

The velocity of the ball bearing increases from zero for 0·8s. The velocity then remains constant at 1·12 m s⁻¹. This is the terminal velocity of the ball bearing in the glycerine.

EXAMPLE 3

A speedboat of mass 800 kg is initially at rest on a lake. The speedboat's engine is started and it produces a constant force of 5 kN. As the speedboat accelerates, the frictional force on it increases. A graph of the force of friction acting on the speedboat against time is shown.

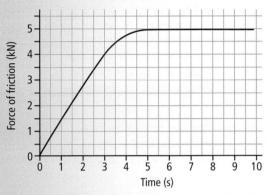

(a) State the force of friction acting on the speedboat 3 s after its engine is switched on.

4 kN

(b) Calculate the acceleration of the speedboat at this time.

Unbalanced force acting on speedboat = 5000 – 4000 = 1000 N

$$a = \frac{F}{m} = \frac{1000}{800} = 1·25 \text{ms}^{-2}$$

(c) Describe and explain the movement of the speedboat after 7 s.

The engine force and frictional forces are balanced. The boat reaches its terminal velocity.

ONLINE TEST

How well have you understood gravity, weightlessness and freefall? Go online and test yourself at www.brightredbooks.net/N5Physics

THINGS TO DO AND THINK ABOUT

1. In October 2012, Felix Baumgartner became the first person to jump from a balloon at height of 39 km above the Earth. During his descent, Felix reached a terminal velocity which was greater than had been experienced by any other skydiver. Investigate why Felix was able to fall faster through the atmosphere than anyone had before.

PROJECTILE MOTION

The key concepts to learn in this topic are:
- how to explain projectile motion
- the use of appropriate relationships to solve problems involving projectile motion from a horizontal launch, including the use of motion graphs
- how to explain satellite orbits in terms of projectile motion
- a qualitative awareness of the relationship between the altitude of a satellite and its period.

DON'T FORGET

On this course, only projectiles which have been launched horizontally will be considered.

Projectiles travelling through the air

PROJECTILES

A **projectile** is any object that has been launched (or projected) into the air. Once in the air, gravity is the only force acting on the projectile (assuming air resistance is negligible).

Horizontally-launched projectiles move outwards away from the launch site as well as falling vertically, and so they move in curved paths.

The projectile's curved path is caused in part by the force of gravity – the object accelerates downwards. At the same time the horizontal velocity stays constant if air resistance is negligible.

Compare one object dropped vertically with another identical object projected horizontally at the same time.

Both objects reach the ground at exactly the *same time*. This result shows that the time of flight for the projectile depends *only* on its initial vertical height, not on its horizontal motion.

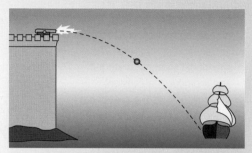

The cannon ball shown here is an example of a projectile that has been launched horizontally

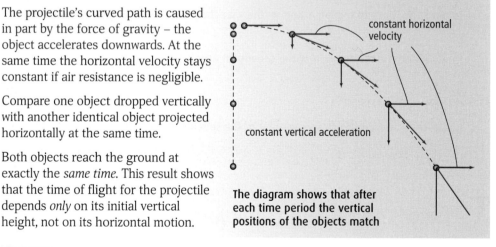

The diagram shows that after each time period the vertical positions of the objects match

DON'T FORGET

The time of flight for a projectile is the same for horizontal and vertical motion.

PROJECTILE MOTION

Projectile motion can be treated as two independent motions. The horizontal motion can be treated separately from the vertical motion when solving numerical examples.
- The horizontal velocity of a projectile stays constant as there are no horizontal forces acting on the projectile (air resistance is negligible).
- The vertical velocity of a projectile increases as the projectile accelerates under the force of gravity, with an acceleration of $9.8\,\text{m}\,\text{s}^{-2}$.

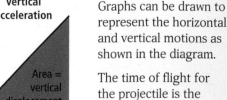

Graphs can be drawn to represent the horizontal and vertical motions as shown in the diagram.

The time of flight for the projectile is the same for the horizontal and vertical motion.

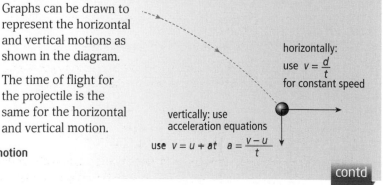

horizontally:
use $v = \dfrac{d}{t}$
for constant speed

vertically: use acceleration equations

use $v = u + at$ $\quad a = \dfrac{v - u}{t}$

Graphs for the horizontal and vertical components of motion

contd

EXAMPLE:

An aircraft flying horizontally at $55\,\text{ms}^{-1}$ drops a package of supplies to earthquake victims. The package has a vertical velocity of $75\,\text{ms}^{-1}$ when it hits the ground.

(a) Calculate the time taken for the package to reach the ground.

$a = \dfrac{v - u}{t}$ for vertical motion, $u = 0$, $v = 75$,

$a = 9\cdot8$

$9\cdot8 = \dfrac{75 - 0}{t}$ so $t = \dfrac{75 - 0}{9.8} = 7\cdot65\,\text{s}$

(b) Calculate the horizontal distance travelled by the package before it reached the ground.

The package is released horizontally, so $v_h = 55\,\text{ms}^{-1}$

$s = vt = 55 \times 7\cdot65 = 421\,\text{m}$

(c) State any assumptions made when carrying out your calculations.

Assume that air resistance has a negligible effect on the package's movement.

ONLINE

For more extended examples go to www. brightredbooks.net/ N5Physics

SATELLITE MOTION

Satellite motion is an extension of projectile motion. The faster a projectile is fired horizontally, the greater the distance it travels before reaching the Earth's surface. The diagram shows a projectile being fired horizontally off a cliff at two different velocities.

The surface of the Earth is flat on this diagram, but the Earth is a sphere so its surface is curved. If a projectile has a fast enough initial horizontal velocity, the shape of its curved path will be the same as the shape of the Earth's curved surface.

The projectile is falling towards the Earth but never reaches the surface – the curved projectile path and the Earth's curvature are the same.

An artificial satellite is put into orbit by launching it from Earth, then giving it the correct horizontal velocity so that it falls back to Earth with a curved path that matches the Earth's curvature.

The satellite motion takes place above the Earth's atmosphere so there is no friction to slow down the satellite.

It is a common misconception that orbiting astronauts are weightless as there is no force of gravity acting on them. This is *not* correct. They *appear* to be weightless as they are in freefall, falling back to Earth at the same rate as their satellite (not because the value of g is zero).

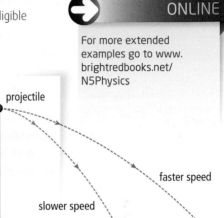

The projectile that is fired at the fastest velocity lands the furthest from the edge of the cliff

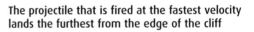

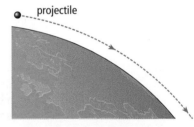

A projectile with a curved path that matches the curvature of the Earth

SATELLITE ALTITUDE AND PERIOD

Today there are many satellites in orbit for a variety of uses, such as communication.

The **period T** of a satellite is the time for it to complete one orbit of the Earth.

The further away the satellite is from the Earth, the longer its period. The International Space Station (ISS) orbits the Earth once every 90 minutes and thus orbits the Earth 16 times each day.

The required height of a satellite's orbit above the Earth's surface usually depends on its use. Satellites in low orbits must travel faster than satellites in higher orbits. The height that allows a satellite to make one orbit in 24 hours is approximately $36\,000\,\text{km}$ above the Earth. At this height, as the satellite orbits, it stays in a fixed position relative to a point on the Earth's surface. Orbits at this height are known as geostationary orbits.

Communications and weather satellites are often placed in geostationary orbits so that they remain connected with the same area on Earth.

A satellite with a curved path around the Earth

ONLINE TEST

How well have you understood projectiles? Go online and test yourself at www.brightredbooks.net/ N5Physics

THINGS TO DO AND THINK ABOUT

1. Carry out research into satellite uses. Obtain information about different types of orbit in relation to a satellite's function. Investigate how it is possible to alter the orbital height of satellites that are already in orbit.

SPACE EXPLORATION 1

The key concept to learn in this topic is:

- an awareness of evidence supporting current understanding of the universe from telescopes and space exploration.

SPACE RESEARCH

Our understanding of the universe is constantly being updated as space exploration continues to produce new information. You should keep up to date with evolving models and should know about recent modifications to our understanding.

Make your own mind up about the research

One way to explore and evaluate current evidence is by visiting respected and legitimate scientific websites. You can then consider:

- whether evidence supports our understanding of the universe and our place within it
- the role of physics in gathering this evidence
- the impact of this understanding on our everyday lives.

By studying today's universe, scientists can discover information which supports different theories about space. This study is done by space exploration, including the use of telescopes.

EVIDENCE SUPPORTING THE CURRENT UNDERSTANDING OF THE UNIVERSE

Signals from space travel at the speed of light. Even travelling at this speed, the signals take a long time to travel the huge distances across the universe. The signals carry information about what was happening a long time ago in the universe. This information can be analysed; it is used to support our understanding of the universe and how it was formed.

Different types of telescope are used to gather signals from space. These signals are from different parts of the electromagnetic spectrum.

ONLINE

Learn more by reading NASA's 'Gamma Ray Telescopes and Detectors' at www.brightredbooks.net/N5Physics

X-ray telescope

TYPES OF TELESCOPE

Gamma ray telescopes

The Earth's atmosphere absorbs much of the gamma radiation from space. So, the gamma radiation from space is studied using gamma ray telescopes carried by satellites in orbit *above* the atmosphere, and also by some ground based detectors.

The Fermi satellite uses a gamma ray telescope to investigate sources of **cosmic rays**. Cosmic rays are thought to be important in the production of gamma radiation from different astronomical objects, such as **supernovae** remains and **black holes**. Investigating the sources of cosmic rays provides data which improves our understanding of the structure and mechanism of supernovae events.

X-ray telescopes

The Earth's atmosphere absorbs many of the X-rays from space. So, these are studied using X-ray telescopes that are carried by satellites in orbit above the atmosphere. Chandra, XMM-Newton and Suzaku are satellite observatories which have X-ray telescopes on board.

contd

Data received from outside our galaxy using these X-ray telescopes indicates the presence of a previously undetected massive cloud of very hot gas. The existence of this cloud is regarded as an important piece of evidence supporting the **big bang model** which describes the origin of the universe.

Ultraviolet telescopes

Data from **ultraviolet radiation** detected from space by the GALEX satellite has contributed to research into how stars are formed inside galaxies. The Hubble satellite also contains an ultraviolet telescope.

Optical telescopes

Light from stars and galaxies viewed through optical telescopes can be analysed to obtain line spectra which identify the chemical elements present in the stars.

Observation and analysis of the motion of distant galaxies suggests that most galaxies are moving *away* from Earth. This supports the 'expanding universe theory' of the standard big bang model.

Infrared telescopes

Study of space using optical telescopes is limited because some astronomical objects lie behind dense regions of dust and gas. Infrared radiation has longer wavelengths than visible light which allow it to travel through these regions of space without being absorbed or scattered.

Infrared telescopes have been used to investigate the structure of distant stars and galaxies. The Spitzer satellite has an infrared telescope which has obtained data that has increased astronomers' understanding of star formation within galaxies.

Infrared telescopes used to detect infrared radiation from space can be land based like this one, or carried on satellites

Radio telescopes

Radio telescopes used to detect radio waves from space can be land-based, or carried on satellites.

Radio waves are emitted from objects in space. Radio telescopes have been used to detect and receive radio waves from pulsars and quasars. They have allowed production of maps showing the positions of galaxies and nebulae.

A land-based radio telescope

COBE and WMAP are satellites which carry radio telescopes. They have obtained data which has provided astronomers with more information about the age of the universe, and the origin and structure of galaxies.

THINGS TO DO AND THINK ABOUT

1. There are many different areas of space research being carried out to improve our current understanding of the universe, especially the standard big bang model. Carry out your own research into one aspect of the big bang model, considering the value of this research. Include a discussion of whether it adds to the understanding of the universe, or contradicts previously understood ideas.

2. Debate with others whether the huge cost of this research is worthwhile. For example, you could debate whether this knowledge has a real impact on our society, or simply adds complicated information which is not useful.

3. Sub-atomic particles feature in the theory of the standard model for the big bang. Find out what these particles are and how they are being investigated today, for example, in the Large Hadron Collider.

4. Investigate the claim by astronomer Edwin Hubble that the velocity of a galaxy depends on its distance from Earth.

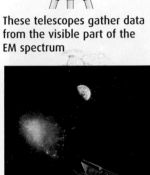

DON'T FORGET

Using satellites to explore and gather data from space has increased our understanding of planet Earth.

These telescopes gather data from the visible part of the EM spectrum

The Spitzer satellite

ONLINE

Check out 'Infrared Telescopes Spy Small, Dark Asteroids' at www.brightredbooks.net/N5Physics

DON'T FORGET

Some satellites are used to detect electromagnetic radiation which cannot penetrate the Earth's atmosphere.

ONLINE TEST

How well have you learned about the different types of telescopes? Take the 'Space Exploration' test at www.brightredbooks.net/N5Physics

SPACE EXPLORATION 2

The key concepts to learn in this topic are:

- an awareness of the benefits of satellites, for example GPS, weather forecasting, communications and space exploration (Hubble telescope, ISS)
- an awareness of the potential benefits of space exploration
- an awareness of the challenges of space travel.

THE BENEFITS OF SATELLITES

Application satellites have had an overwhelming effect on day-to-day living for mankind. These are satellites which have been placed in orbit for a specific purpose.

There is a huge range of uses for these satellites:

- worldwide communication and data transfer – this has improved communications, and has had an impact on the everyday lives of many people
- global and local weather information and forecasting, including tracking of hurricanes and other storm systems
- monitoring of long-term climate change – this has highlighted the importance of reducing activities which lead to global warming
- pollution monitoring – this has identified areas of the planet where people are suffering from the effects of pollution (for example, some parts of the world are affected by exposure to increased ultraviolet radiation resulting from deterioration of the ozone layer by pollution)
- provision of Global Positioning Systems – satellite navigation is commonly used today
- military observations
- commercial entertainment – satellite broadcasting television channels now mean that events can be viewed worldwide almost as they happen.

Satellites have had a huge impact on everyday life for most people. For instance, weather forecasting has become very accurate by using instant data from satellites. This has helped, for example, farmers to know the best times to plant and harvest crops.

Satellite uses

THE BENEFITS OF SPACE EXPLORATION

Scientists and engineers develop technology and equipment for space exploration. Much of this technology has been modified and developed for use in everyday life for the benefit of mankind.

There have been many medical benefits which developed from space research:

- Space research led to the development of devices to measure the amount of infrared radiation emitted from distant stars and planets. This expertise was used to produce infrared thermometers which determine body temperature accurately by measuring the infrared radiation emitted from the inner ear, without actually being in contact with a patient. This has greatly reduced the instances of cross infection.

Thermometer that measures infrared radiation emitted from the body

- Water purification devices designed for use during space travel have been adapted to help patients with kidney disease.
- Technology which was developed to improve images of the moon has been adapted for use with body imaging scanning devices.

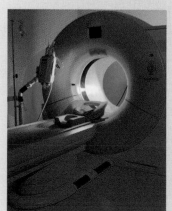

MRI scanners developed from technology that was used to observe the moon

THE CHALLENGES OF SPACE TRAVEL

Travelling large distances in space.

Rocket engines use a huge amount of conventional fuel at launch simply to propel a spacecraft into space. These rocket engines are discarded after the launch into space. The spacecraft itself has a limited capacity for conventional fuel.

Space exploration of other planets requires vast distances to be travelled. Once launched, spacecraft have to be able to travel at high speeds to reach distant destinations in a reasonable time. Possible solutions for travelling large distance in space have already been developed:

Ion drive engine

An ion drive engine produces a beam of gas ions. When these ions are expelled with a force (thrust) from the engine nozzle, there is a reaction force on the nozzle. This reaction force causes acceleration of the spacecraft. This force is typically very small, and, using $a = \frac{F}{m}$, means that the acceleration is very small. The ion thrust engine must operate for a long time before the spacecraft reaches its top speed. The electrical energy required to operate the ion drive is obtained from a solar panel array or a nuclear generator.

NASA's Dawn Probe was launched in 2006 on a journey to the distant asteroid belt which lies between Mars and Jupiter, to study the asteroid Vesta and dwarf planet Ceres. The Probe, which uses an ion drive propulsion system powered by a solar panel array, was launched in September 2007. It reached Vesta in July 2011, and Ceres in March 2015.

An artist's impression of Deep Space 1's ion drive engine

Gravity assist

Gravity assist (sometimes known as a 'gravitational slingshot') is a technique which allows a spacecraft to increase its speed by 'flying by' a planet. As the spacecraft approaches the planet, a gravitational attractive force will cause the spacecraft to start orbiting the planet. The planet is moving in orbit around the sun. When the spacecraft leaves this orbit some of the kinetic energy of the planet is transferred to it, and its speed increases.

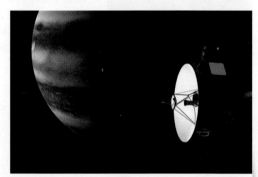

On its mission to study the dwarf planet Pluto, the NASA spacecraft New Horizons used this gravity assist technique by flying close to the planet Jupiter, to increase its speed and so shorten its overall journey time to Pluto.

New Horizons completing a gravity assist fly by of Jupiter

Manoeuvring a spacecraft in orbit

Spacecraft docking with another orbiting object (such as the International Space Station) requires small thruster rockets to be fired carefully to align both vehicles. In space orbit around the Earth or other planets, there is very little friction because of the reduced atmosphere. The thrusters expel exhaust gases with a small force. There is an opposite reaction force according to Newton's third law which causes the spaceship to move in the opposite direction.

THINGS TO DO AND THINK ABOUT

Use internet search engines to investigate the uses of some of the satellites mentioned. Find out about the sensors that a satellite uses to obtain information, where it was launched, how it obtains its energy, and its lifespan.

ONLINE

Read more about ion drive engines at www.brightredbooks.net/N5Physics

DON'T FORGET

Space exploration has helped our understanding of the universe, and has produced many benefits for people.

ONLINE TEST

How well have you learned about space exploration? Test yourself at www.brightredbooks.net/N5Physics

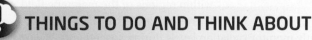

SPACE EXPLORATION 3

The key concepts to learn in this topic are:

- how sufficient energy is maintained to operate life support systems in a spacecraft
- an awareness of the risks associated with manned space exploration.

The Rosetta spacecraft with extended solar panel arrays

The curiosity space vehicle on Mars uses an RTG as an energy source

ONLINE

Check out NASA's Orion program at www.brightredbooks.net

NASA's Launch Abort System (LAS)

MAINTAINING SUFFICIENT ENERGY TO OPERATE LIFE SUPPORT SYSTEMS

During a long manned voyage in space, electrical energy is required to operate equipment in the spacecraft to maintain a suitable temperature, produce oxygen and water and to remove waste gases from the air. This electrical energy is also used to recharge batteries.

Solar (photovoltaic) cells are used to transform solar into electrical energy, and usually recharge batteries for use when the panels are shaded from the sun. As a spacecraft moves further away from the sun, the solar energy falling on the cells reduces. Using current technology, solar cells are practical for spacecraft operating at a distance up to the orbit of Mars. One suggestion is to increase the size of the solar cell array as the spacecraft travels further away from the sun.

Radioisotope thermoelectric generators

(RTGs) use radioactive material which produces heat energy when it decays. The heat energy is converted into electrical energy by devices called thermocouples. Plutonium-238 is commonly used as the source radioactive element. Currently, the typical electrical power output from this type of generator is quite low; however several could be combined to provide greater power.

THE RISKS ASSOCIATED WITH MANNED SPACE EXPLORATION

Launching a space rocket

There are many difficulties connected with the launching of a space vehicle. Vast amounts of fuel have to be carried on the rocket to maintain the thrust of the rocket's engines as it accelerates into space. This means that take-off is a very dangerous time for the astronauts. Once a rocket has been launched, the astronauts are at risk until they have been safely delivered in their spacecraft into orbit.

NASA is currently developing space rocket technology to take astronauts further into space beyond an Earth orbit, with a safe return. An escape vehicle (Launch Abort System) has been developed which will pull astronauts away from a falling rocket, and allow astronauts to land safely in the ocean using parachutes, if a problem arises at take-off.

Potential exposure to radiation in space

Radiation in space consists mainly of high energy ionising particles which could harm humans if they are not protected. The main sources of these particles are

- cosmic rays originating from deep space
- solar flares
- ionising particles which are held within regions of the magnetic field surrounding the Earth.

On board instruments constantly monitor radiation levels during spaceflights. Beyond the Earth's magnetic field, radiation levels can become potentially lethal. Research is constantly being carried out to find ways of minimising the risks of over exposure to crew members if more distant space manned exploration is undertaken.

Withstanding the pressure differences in space

When a spacecraft leave the Earth's atmosphere, the air pressure outside the spacecraft reduces. In space, the pressure is reduced to near vacuum levels. The cabin pressure

contd

must be maintained to allow the occupants to survive. This means that the spacecraft must be able to withstand a huge pressure difference between the inside and the outside of the cabin. This also requires a complex system to monitor and maintain life support systems to maintain the oxygen, temperature and pressure levels necessary for survival.

Re-entry to a planet's atmosphere

Space vehicles and astronauts have to survive the descent through the Earth's atmosphere on their return.

When returning from orbit or space, the spacecraft has a huge amount of kinetic energy. As the spacecraft gets closer to the Earth's surface, its speed and kinetic energy must be reduced.

This kinetic energy is gradually transferred into heat energy as the spacecraft leaves orbit and enters the Earth's atmosphere. The return of the spacecraft has to be controlled as it returns from its orbit. If the angle of descent is too shallow, the spacecraft would bounce off the atmosphere and return into orbit and, if its descent is too steep, too much heat energy would be produced in a short time, destroying the craft. Passengers and cargo must be protected from extremely high temperatures. Returning spacecraft are fitted with a 'heat shield' material to insulate and protect occupants from excessive temperatures.

NASA's Orion Space capsule's return to Earth

There are two methods of descent for the dissipation of heat energy during re-entry:

1. Re-entry using *flight descent* – for large spacecraft, a huge amount of kinetic energy has to be transferred into heat energy. A lengthy time of descent is required so that the rate of heating is reduced to a manageable level. The spacecraft has to be able to fly (or glide since it has no engines) through the atmosphere to descend at this lower rate. The Space Shuttle was an example of a spacecraft which had a controlled flight descent. When it landed, it did so as a conventional aircraft on a long runway. Flight descent to Earth requires the spacecraft structure to have wings. The protruding wings cause problems with heating at the start of re-entry.

The Space Shuttle looked much like a conventional aircraft on re-entry

2. Re-entry using *ballistic descent* – this type of descent is when the spacecraft is steered into the atmosphere to return, almost in freefall, directly to the surface. Ballistic re-entry takes a short time (typically less than 1 hour). Once the descent has started, there is limited control which can be exerted on the craft, except before deploying parachutes when it is close to the Earth's surface. Only part of the spacecraft (the 'descent module' in the Soyuz Spacecraft programme), designed with a specific shape to protect the interior from overheating, can be used in this type of re-entry. One disadvantage of this method is that the size of the descent module is also limited. Much of the mass of the returning descent module consists of its heat shield, which protects the occupants or cargo from the heat produced around the descent module on re-entry.

A spacecraft's heat shield has several features to help reduce the heating of the interior.

Some heat shields use a complex process known as ***ablation***. One ablation process during re-entry involves disintegration of the surface material of the heat shield at extreme temperatures, removing heat energy as the material leaves the shield. Another ablation process occurs at high temperature when some of the material inside the heat shield changes state into gas, absorbing **latent heat energy** of vaporisation. The pressure of the gas forces it out of the heat shield, removing more heat energy. The escaping gases also prevent external hot gases from reaching the module. The Soyuz descent module, and NASA's Orion spacecraft uses a heat shield which ablates.

Some heat shields use a process known as *dissipation*. The heat energy is absorbed by insulating tiles which cover the spacecraft. Some of the absorbed heat energy is then re-radiated from the spacecraft back into the atmosphere, to maintain an acceptable temperature level inside the manned compartment. The Space Shuttle used dissipation.

DON'T FORGET

You need to know about the problems associated with re-entry into the Earth's atmosphere.

ONLINE TEST

How well have you learned about this topic? Take the 'Space Exploration' test at www.brightredbooks.net/N5Physics

THINGS TO DO AND THINK ABOUT

Carry out internet research into the risks and challenges associated with manned space exploration. Visit reputable websites such as the National Aeronautics and Space Administration (NASA) and the European Space Agency (ESA), to discover the current research and what the latest projects for exploration are.

(a) Which type of galaxy is the largest?   **1**

Elliptical galaxies.

(b) Why do elliptical galaxies contain few new stars?   **1**

New stars are formed in dust and gas clouds – elliptical galaxies contain little dust and few gas clouds.

(c) Show that the diameter of Messier 87 is $1\cdot14 \times 10^{21}$ m.   **3**

$d = vt$ $d = 3 \times 10^8 \times (365\cdot25 \times 24 \times 60 \times 60) \times 120\,000$ $d = 1\cdot14 \times 10^{21}$ m

Total marks 5

Questions based on an application of the course content

This type of question usually consists of several parts and asks you to apply knowledge and skills. There is usually an introduction (with a diagram) which describes the application.

The application usually contains a description of a machine or a system which is commonly used. It may even refer to the latest technology or to a new invention. You may be asked to calculate or deduce answers based on your knowledge of the coursework.

Example 7

A halogen heater contains two heater tubes which can be switched on separately. The heater also has an 'uplighter' lamp that can be switched on to illuminate the ceiling.

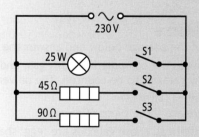

The heater has three different heat settings: LOW, MEDIUM and HIGH. These settings can be produced by switching on the heating tubes.

The circuit diagram for the heater is shown.

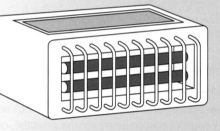

(a) When switch S1 is closed, the lamp operates at its rating of 25 W.
Calculate the current in the lamp.   **3**

$I = \dfrac{P}{V} = \dfrac{25}{230} = 0\cdot11\,\text{A}$

(b) Switch S1 is opened and switches S2 and S3 are closed.

(i) Calculate the combined resistance of both heater tubes.   **3**

$\dfrac{1}{R_T} = \dfrac{1}{R_1} + \dfrac{1}{R_2}$ $\dfrac{1}{R_T} = \dfrac{1}{45} + \dfrac{1}{90}$ $R_T = 30\,\Omega$

(ii) Calculate the total power developed in the heating elements when S2 and S3 are closed.   **3**

$P = \dfrac{V^2}{R} = \dfrac{230^2}{30} = 1763\cdot3\,\text{W}$

(iii) State and explain which switch or switches would have to be closed to produce the LOW heat setting.   **3**

S3 (only).

Greatest value of resistance gives lowest current.

Since $P = I^2R$ this gives lowest power output

Total marks 12

DATA SHEET

Speed of light in materials

Material	Speed in ms^{-1}
Air	3.0×10^8
Carbon dioxide	3.0×10^8
Diamond	1.2×10^8
Glass	2.0×10^8
Glycerol	2.1×10^8
Water	2.3×10^8

Gravitational field strengths

	Gravitational field strength on the surface in Nkg^{-1}
Earth	9.8
Jupiter	23
Mars	3.7
Mercury	3.7
Moon	1.6
Neptune	11
Saturn	9.0
Sun	270
Uranus	8.7
Venus	8.9

Specific latent heat of fusion of materials

Material	Specific latent heat of fusion in Jkg^{-1}
Alcohol	0.99×10^5
Aluminium	3.95×10^5
Carbon dioxide	1.80×10^5
Copper	2.05×10^5
Iron	2.67×10^5
Lead	0.25×10^5
Water	3.35×10^5

Specific latent heat of vaporization of materials

Material	Specific latent heat of vaporisation in Jkg-1
Alcohol	11.2×10^5
Carbon Dioxide	3.77×10^5
Glycerol	8.30×10^5
Turpentine	2.90×10^5
Water	22.6×10^5

Speed of sound in materials

Material	Speed in ms^{-1}
Aluminium	5200
Air	340
Bone	4100
Carbon dioxide	270
Glycerol	1900
Muscle	1600
Steel	5200
Tissue	1500
Water	1500

Specific heat capacity of materials

Material	Specific heat capacity in Jkg^{-1}°C
Alcohol	2350
Aluminium	902
Copper	386
Glass	500
Ice	2100
Iron	480
Lead	128
Oil	2130
Water	4180

Melting and boiling points of materials

Material	Melting point in °C	Boiling point in °C
Alcohol	−98	65
Aluminium	660	2470
Copper	1077	2567
Glycerol	18	290
Lead	328	1737
Iron	1537	2737

Radiation weighting factors

Type of radiation	Radiation weighting factor
Alpha	20
Beta	1
Fast neutrons	10
Gamma	1
Slow neutrons	3

RELATIONSHIPS REQUIRED FOR NATIONAL 5 PHYSICS

$E_p = mgh$

$E_k = \frac{1}{2} mv^2$

$Q = It$

$V = IR$

$R_T = R_1 + R_2 + \ldots$

$\frac{1}{R_T} = \frac{1}{R_1} + \frac{1}{R_2} + \ldots$

$V_2 = \frac{R_2}{R_1 + R_2} V_s$

$\frac{V_1}{V_2} = \frac{R_1}{R_2}$

$P = \frac{E}{t}$

$P = IV$

$P = I^2 R$

$P = \frac{V^2}{R}$

$E_h = cm\Delta T$

$p = \frac{F}{A}$

$\frac{pV}{T} = \text{constant}$

$p_1 V_1 = p_2 V_2$

$\frac{p_1}{T_1} = \frac{p_2}{T_2}$

$\frac{V_1}{T_1} = \frac{V_2}{T_2}$

$d = vt$

$v = f\lambda$

$T = \frac{1}{f}$

$A = \frac{N}{t}$

$D = \frac{E}{m}$

$H = Dw_R$

$\dot{H} = \frac{H}{t}$

$s = vt$

$d = \bar{v}t$

$s = \bar{v}t$

$a = \frac{v - u}{t}$

$W = mg$

$F = ma$

$E_w = Fd$

$E_h = ml$

GLOSSARY

absorbed dose (*D*)   The amount of energy per kilogram (of human tissue) received from exposure to nuclear radiation.

absolute zero   The lowest temperature on the kelvin temperature scale, 0 kelvin (−273 °C).

absorption   When materials absorb the energy of nuclear radiation.

Acceleration, *a* (m s⁻²)   The rate of change of velocity (positive or negative) in unit time, calculated using $a = (v - u)/t$.

activity (becquerels, Bq)   The number of atoms in a radioactive substance that disintegrate per unit time.

air resistance   A frictional force acting on objects which move through air (sometimes called 'drag').

alpha particle, alpha radiation   Radiation caused by a relatively large, slow moving radioactive particle with a positive charge (a helium nucleus).

alternating current (a.c.)   The periodic movement of electric charge between the supply terminals.

ammeter   An instrument for measuring electric current.

amperes (A)   Unit of electric current, also amps.

amplitude   The peak value of an alternating quantity, e.g. a wave. The height of a wave measured from the mid position to the crest (or trough) of the wave.

angle of incidence   The angle that a ray of light makes with the normal before it passes into a medium, e.g. glass.

angle of refraction   The angle that a ray of light makes with the normal when it passes into a medium, e.g. glass.

atom   A basic unit of matter, composed of protons, neutrons, and electrons.

average speed, $\bar{v}$ (m s⁻¹)   The speed of an object over a relatively long period of time or distance.

average velocity, $\bar{v}$ (m s⁻¹)   The speed and direction of an object over a relatively long period of time or distance.

background radiation   Radiation in the atmosphere due to various natural and man-made radioactive sources.

battery   Two or more electric cells which transfer electrical energy to charges.

becquerels (Bq)   The unit of activity of a radioactive substance where one becquerel is one decay (of an atom) per second.

beta particle, beta radiation   Radiation caused by a relatively small, fast moving radioactive particle with a negative charge (electron).

big bang model/theory   Current theory of the formation of the universe.

black hole   A space where the gravitational force is so strong that even light cannot escape, sometimes caused when stars collapse.

capacitor   An electronic component which stores charge.

chain reaction   A neutron hits a uranium nucleus causing it to split (fission). This produces heat energy and more neutrons, which in turn cause more fission events to take place.

chemical energy   Energy produced from chemical compounds, including coal, oil and gas.

concave   The shape of lens that causes light rays to diverge.

condensation   When a gas changes state into a liquid.

conductor   A material which allows charge to move through it easily.

conservation of energy   The total energy before and after a transformation from one form into another is unchanged.

convex   The shape of lens that causes light rays to converge to a focus.

cosmic rays   High energy particles which arrive at Earth from space.

crest   The topmost part of a wave shape.

current (*I*)   The flow of charge per unit time measured in amperes.

deceleration (m s⁻²)   The rate of change of velocity, i.e. change in velocity divided by the time taken when an object is slowing down.

diffraction   A property of waves whereby they 'bend' around a gap or obstacle.

diode   An electrical component which allows current through it in one direction only.

direct current (d.c.)   The movement of charge which is always in one direction between the terminals of the supply.

displacement   The direct distance of a finishing point from a starting point, including the direction.

electrical energy   Type of energy associated with electric charge.

electromagnetic (EM) spectrum   Waves which range from long wavelength radio waves to gamma with short wavelengths. They all travel at the speed of light (3×10^8 m s⁻¹).

electromagnetic waves   The waves of the electromagnetic spectrum.

energy (joules, J)   The ability of an object or system to do work.

energy transformation   Describes how energy from one source is changed into another energy source, e.g. $E_p \rightarrow E_k$.

equivalent dose (*H*)   A measure of the effect that exposure to radiation has on humans, measured in Sieverts (Sv).

equivalent dose rate ($\dot{H}$)   A measure of the rate of absorption of nuclear radiation by humans.

filament lamp   A type of lamp that uses a metal resistance wire to transform electrical energy to light (and heat).

film badge   A monitoring device worn by people who work with radioactive materials to record the type and quantity of any exposure to radiation.

fission   The process of splitting the nucleus of an atom into smaller nuclei and releasing energy.

force (N)   A pull or a push, measured in newtons. One newton is the force required to give a mass of one kilogram the acceleration of 1 m s⁻².

freefall   Describes the motion of an object falling freely due to the force of gravity.

frequency (hertz, Hz)   The number of events per second or waves which pass a point in one second.

friction   A force that acts in the opposite direction to objects as they move or try to move.

fusion (1)   This is the process of joining two smaller atoms (or nuclei) to produce a larger atom with the release of energy.

(2)   The change of state of a substance from solid to liquid.

gamma camera   A device containing a detector of gamma radiation.

gamma radiation, gamma rays   A group of waves emitted by some radioactive materials, part of the EM spectrum.

Geiger–Muller tube   A radiation detector, usually connected to a counter device, which can detect alpha, beta and gamma radiation.

geostationary orbit   An orbit above the equator in which a satellite takes 24 hours to orbit the Earth.

gravitational field strength (*g*)   The weight per unit mass (or the force of gravity acting on each kilogram) used to calculate the weight of an object.

gray (Gy)   The unit for absorbed dose.

half-life   The time for the activity of a radioactive substance to reduce (or decay) to half its original value.

infrared (IR) radiation   Also known as heat rays or waves, a group of waves which are part of the electromagnetic spectrum.

interference   A property of waves whereby waves from different sources can combine (not in this course).

ion   An atom which has lost or gained one or more electrons, becoming a charged particle.

ionisation   When nuclear radiation changes atoms into ions.

isotope   Different forms of the same element, with different numbers of neutrons in the nucleus, but with the same atomic number.

kinetic energy (E_k)   Energy an object possesses when moving.

kinetic theory of gases   An explanation of the behaviour of particles in a gas in terms of the volume, pressure and temperature of the gas.

latent heat   The energy required to change the state of a substance.

light year   The distance travelled by light in one year.

longitudinal wave   Waves in which the particles transferring energy vibrate in the direction of travel, e.g. sound waves.

medium   The material which waves travel through, e.g. water, glass.

microwaves   A group of waves which are part of the electromagnetic spectrum with wavelengths that are shorter than those of radio waves.

Newton's laws of motion   First, second and third laws identify the effect of forces on objects.

normal   A line drawn at right angles to an edge (usually of glass), used when drawing ray diagrams to represent the path of light waves.

nuclear fusion   Two nuclei of small mass combine to form a larger nuclei with release of energy.

oscilloscope   An electrical device with a screen that is used to display electrical signals which can demonstrate wave motion.

period (T)   The time taken for one wave to be produced.

potential difference (p.d.)   A measure of how much energy is transferred to charges in a circuit.

potential energy (E_p)   The stored energy of an object; e.g. an object that has been raised above ground level gains (gravitational) potential energy.

prism   Triangular three-dimensional glass block which is used to refract light rays, usually to analyse the frequencies of light present in the rays.

projectile   An object which has been launched (or projected) into the air.

radiation weighting factor (w_R)   A measure of the harmful effect on human tissue of nuclear radiation.

radio signals or waves   Electromagnetic waves which are part of the electromagnetic spectrum with high frequency and short wavelength.

radionuclide   An isotope of a radioactive element.

reflection   A property of waves whereby they return when reaching a reflective barrier.

refraction   A property of waves whereby the waves change speed (and sometimes direction) when passing from one medium into another, e.g. light waves passing from air into glass.

resultant   The result of adding two (or more) vectors.

resistance   A measure of the opposition to the movement of charge in a circuit.

satellite   An object orbiting a star or planet.

scalar   A physical quantity which has size only.

shielding   The process of, or material required, to absorb radiation to prevent exposure of humans to its effects.

sievert (Sv)   The unit for equivalent dose, H.

speed (v)   The distance travelled by an object per unit of time ($m\,s^{-1}$).

specific heat capacity (c)   The amount of heat energy required to raise the temperature of 1 kg of a substance by 1 °C.

streamlining   The effect of reducing the air resistance (or 'drag') of a moving object, making the object's shape more 'aerodynamic'.

supernova   The result of an explosion of a massive star in space (plural supernovae).

television wave   Electromagnetic waves which are part of the electromagnetic spectrum with high frequency and short wavelength.

terminal velocity   The velocity reached by a moving object when the forces acting on it are balanced.

thrust   Used to describe the force produced by an engine (e.g. rocket engine).

tracer   A radioactive material injected into a human to help with the diagnosis of particular health problems.

transmitter   A device which sends out or produces waves.

transverse wave   Waves where the particles transferring energy vibrate at right angles to direction of travel, e.g. water waves.

trough   The lowest part of a wave shape.

ultraviolet (UV) radiation   A group of waves which are part of the electromagnetic spectrum.

vaporisation   The change of state of a substance from liquid to gas.

vector   A physical quantity which has size and direction.

velocity (v)   The displacement of an object per unit of time, including the direction of the object ($m\,s^{-1}$).

vibration   A backward and forward motion, which usually produces waves.

visible spectrum   Name given to the range of wavelengths of visible light waves giving a range of colours.

wave equation   An equation linking wavespeed, v, frequency, f, and wavelength, λ: $v = f\lambda$.

wavelength (λ)   The length of one wave, the distance from one position on a stream of waves to the next identical position where a new wave starts (m).

wavespeed (v)   The speed at which waves travel through a medium ($m\,s^{-1}$).

weight (W)   The gravitational force acting on an object (N).

work done (E_w)   The amount of energy required when a force, F, is applied to move an object a distance, d. ($E_w = Fd$) (J).

X-rays   Fast-moving electrons referred to as waves which are part of the EM spectrum.